Science Notebook

Glencoe Science

Active Reading Note-taking Guide
Science Grade 8

Consultant
Douglas Fisher, Ph.D.

New York, New York Columbus, Ohio Chicago, Illinois Peoria, Illinois Woodland Hills, California

About the Consultant

Douglas Fisher, Ph.D., is a Professor in the Department of Teacher Education at San Diego State University. He is the recipient of an International Reading Association Celebrate Literacy Award as well as a Christa McAuliffe award for Excellence in Teacher Education. He has published numerous articles on reading and literacy, differentiated instruction, and curriculum design as well as books, such as *Improving Adolescent Literacy: Strategies at Work* and *Responsive Curriculum Design in Secondary Schools: Meeting the Diverse Needs of Students.* He has taught a variety of courses in SDSU's teacher-credentialing program as well as graduate-level courses on English language development and literacy. He also has taught classes in English, writing, and literacy development to secondary school students.

The McGraw·Hill Companies

Send all inquiries to:
Glencoe/McGraw-Hill
8787 Orion Place
Columbus, Ohio 43240-4027

ISBN-13: 978-0-07-879445-2
ISBN-10: 0-07-879445-5

Printed in the United States of America.

16 17 18 19 20 QDB 15 14 13 12

Table of Contents

Table of Contents

Note-Taking Tips

Your notes are a reminder of what you learned in class. Taking good notes can help you succeed in science. These tips will help you take better notes.

- Be an active listener. Listen for important concepts. Pay attention to words, examples, and/or diagrams your teacher emphasizes.
- Write your notes as clearly and concisely as possible. The following symbols and abbreviations may be helpful in your note-taking.

Word or Phrase	Symbol or Abbreviation
for example	e.g.
that is	i.e.
with	w/
without	w/o

Word or Phrase	Symbol or Abbreviation
and	+
approximately	≈
therefore	∴
versus	vs

- Use a symbol such as a star (★) or an asterisk (*) to emphasize important concepts. Place a question mark (?) next to anything that you do not understand.
- Ask questions and participate in class discussion.
- Draw and label pictures or diagrams to help clarify a concept.

Note-Taking Don'ts

- **Don't** write every word. Concentrate on the main ideas and concepts.
- **Don't** use someone else's notes—they may not make sense.
- **Don't** doodle. It distracts you from listening actively.
- **Don't** lose focus or you will become lost in your note-taking.

Using Your Science Notebook

This note-taking guide is designed to help you succeed in learning science content. Each chapter includes:

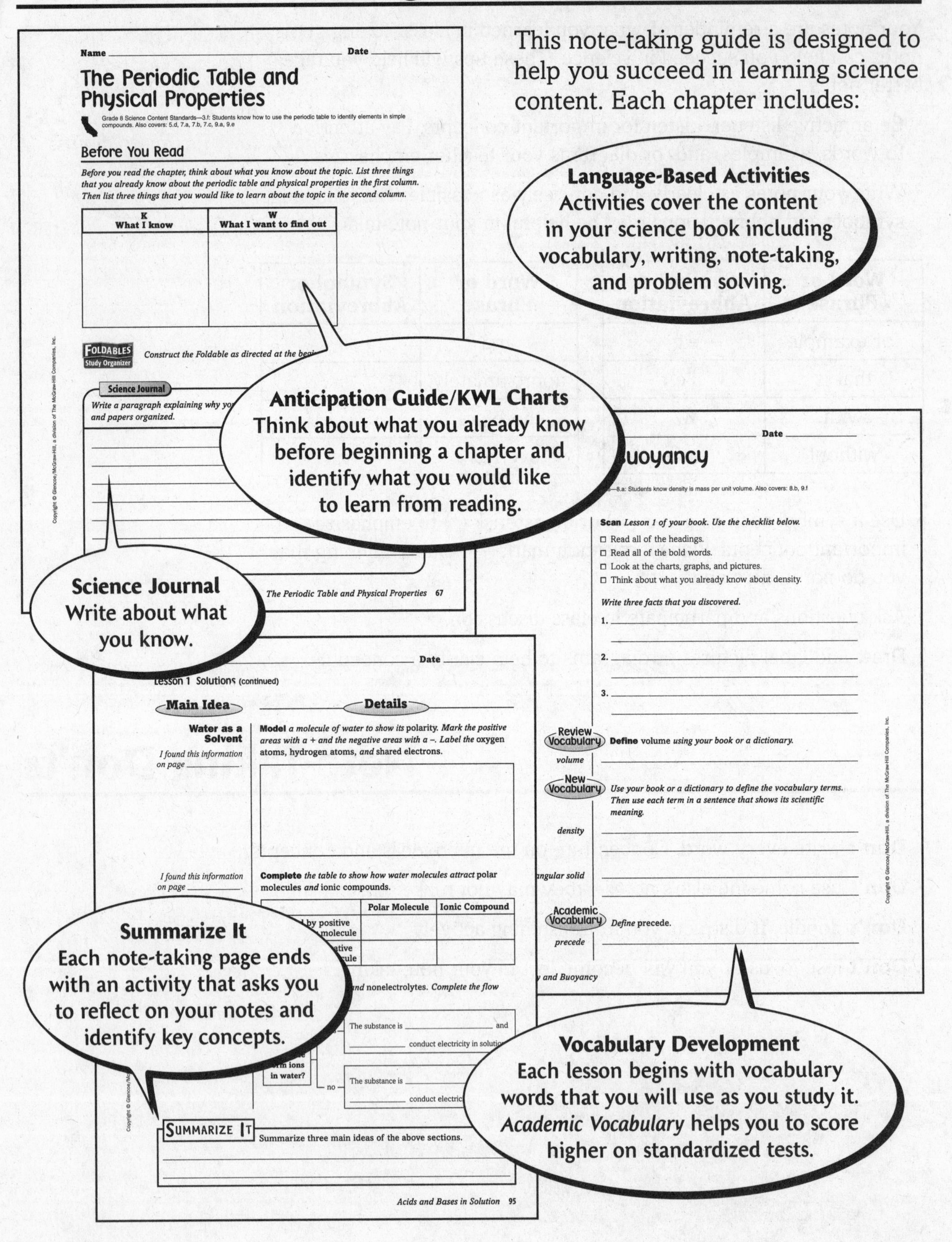

Name ________________________________ Date __________

Lesson 1 Solids, Liquids, and Gases (continued)

Main Idea | **Details**

Solids — *I found this information on page ______.*

Identify *the main* characteristics of solids.

Liquids — *I found this information on page ______.*

Compare *characteristics of* solids *and* liquids.

	Solids	Liquids
Shape	fixed	
Volume		fixed
Motion of particles		

Gases — *I found this information on page ______.*

Organize *information about* gases *in the outline.*

Characteristics of gases

1. Gas particles
   a. ______
   b. ______
2. Shape and volume of gases
   a. ______
   b. ______

SUMMARIZE IT Summarize three main ideas from the above sections.

Note-Taking Based on the Cornell Two-Column Format
Practice effective note-taking through the use of graphic organizers, outlines, and written summaries.

Chapter Wrap-Up
This brings the information together for you. Revisiting what you thought at the beginning of the chapter provides another opportunity for you to discuss what you have learned.

Name ________________________________ Date __________

The Periodic Table and Physical Properties Chapter Wrap-Up

Review the ideas you listed in the table at the beginning of the chapter. Cross out any incorrect information in the first column. Then complete the table by filling in the third .

K What I know	W What I want to find out	L What I learned

Review

Use this checklist to help you study.

- ☐ Review the information you included in your Fo... ble.
- ☐ Study your *Science Notebook* on this chapter.
- ☐ Study the definitions of vocabulary word...
- ☐ Review daily homework assignm...
- ☐ Re-read the chapter and revi...
- ☐ Review the Standards Ch...
- ☐ Look over the Standards...

SUMMARIZE IT Afte... sentences for each lesson to il...

The Periodic Tabl...

Review Checklist
This list helps you assess what you have learned and prepare for your chapter tests.

Name ________________________________ Date __________

Lesson 1 Chemical Properties and Changes (continued)

Main Idea | **Details**

I found this information on page ______.

Identify *six examples of* physical properties of matter.

Examples of Physical Properties of Matter	
1.	4.
2.	5.
3.	6.

Chemical and Physical Changes — *I found this information on page ______.*

Compare and contrast chemical changes *and* physical changes *by completing the Venn diagram, using the phrases listed.*

- properties of substance change
- can often be reversed
- not easily reversed
- forms new substance
- identity of substance does not change
- dissolving is an example
- burning is an example
- includes changes of state

Chemical Change | Both | Physical Change

SUMMARIZE IT Summarize three main ideas of the above sections.

82 *Chemical Reactions*

Graphic Organizers
A variety of visual organizers help you to analyze and summarize information and remember content.

Name ______________________________ Date __________

Motion

Grade 8 Science Content Standards—1.c: Students know how to solve problems involving distance, time, and average speed. Also covers: 1.a, 1.b, 1.d, 1.e, 1.f, 9.d, 9.e

Before You Read

Before you read the chapter, think about what you know about the topic. List three things that you already know about motion in the first column. Then list three things that you would like to learn about motion in the second column.

K What I know	W What I want to find out

Construct the Foldable as directed at the beginning of this chapter.

Science Journal

Write a short description of how the motion of the racers might change from the start of the race to the finish line.

Name ______________________ Date ____________

Motion

Lesson 1 Determining Position

Grade 8 Science Content Standards—1.a: Students know position is defined in relation to some choice of a standard reference point and a set of reference directions.

Scan *Lesson 1 of your book. Use the checklist below.*

- ☐ Read all of the headings.
- ☐ Read all of the bold words.
- ☐ Look at the charts, graphs, and pictures.
- ☐ Think about what you already know about determining position.

Write three things that you learn about determining position.

1. ______________________

2. ______________________

3. ______________________

Review Vocabulary

Define distance.

distance ______________________

New Vocabulary

Write a paragraph, using all of the vocabulary terms.

reference point ______________________

displacement ______________________

vector ______________________

____

____

____

Academic Vocabulary

Use a dictionary to define dimension. *Then use it in a sentence to show its scientific meaning.*

dimension ______________________

____

Name ____________________ Date __________

Main Idea | **Details**

Position and reference point

I found this information on page ________.

Identify *three pieces of information needed to describe an object's* position.

1. ____________________
2. ____________________
3. ____________________

I found this information on page ________.

Summarize *how* + and – signs *are used to show direction.*

____

____

I found this information on page ________.

Organize *information about* vectors. *Complete the diagram.*

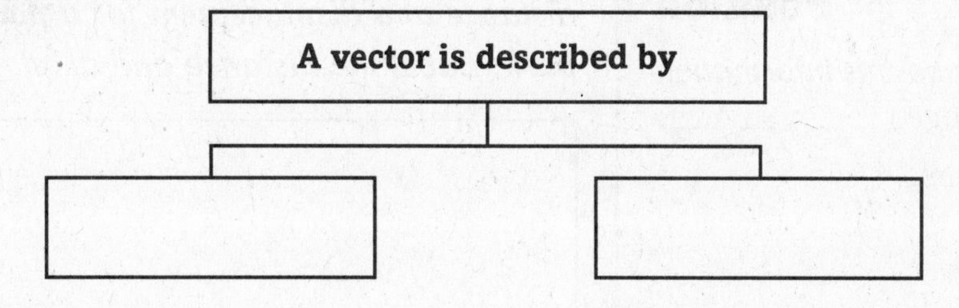

Position in Two Dimensions

I found this information on page ________.

Analyze *why a map uses two reference directions to describe position.*

____

____

____

SUMMARIZE IT Summarize the main ideas of the above sections in three bullet points.

____

____

____

____

____

Name ______________________________ Date ____________

Main Idea | **Details**

Position in Two Dimensions

I found this information on page ____________.

Model *how to* locate a position *using two reference directions. Label the* x-axis, y-axis, *and* origin. *Then put a dot at the position that is 20 m east and 10 m north of the origin. Each mark on the axes represents 10 m.*

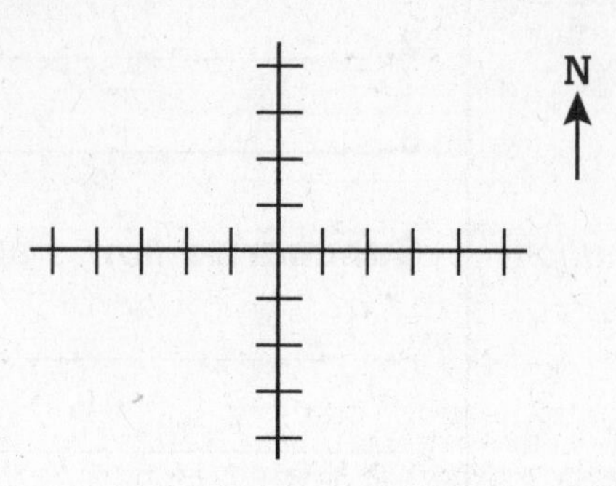

Changing Position

I found this information on page ____________.

Contrast distance *and* displacement. *Draw a diagram to show distance and displacement for a person moving halfway around a park. Label the distance and displacement.*

SUMMARIZE IT Summarize three main ideas of the above sections in three bullet points.

____

____

____

Name ______________________ Date ______________

Motion

Lesson 2 Speed, Velocity, and Acceleration

Grade 8 Science Content Standards—1.c: Students know how to solve problems involving distance, time, and average speed. Also covers: 1.b, 1.d, 1.e

Skim *the headings in Lesson 2 of your book. Identify four topics that will be discussed.*

1. ______________________
2. ______________________
3. ______________________
4. ______________________

Review Vocabulary **Define** rate *using your book or a dictionary.*

rate ______________________

New Vocabulary *Use your book or a dictionary to define the vocabulary terms.*

speed ______________________

constant speed ______________________

instantaneous speed ______________________

average speed ______________________

velocity ______________________

acceleration ______________________

Academic Vocabulary **Define** constant, *using a dictionary.*

constant ______________________

Name ______________________ Date __________

Main Idea | **Details**

What is speed?

I found this information on page ________.

Create *a graphic organizer to contrast* constant speed *and* changing speed. *Include at least four facts.*

What is average speed?

I found this information on page ________.

Summarize *how to* calculate average speed. *Complete the formula with words. Then write it in symbols, and identify the unit used to measure speed.*

average speed = $\frac{\square}{\square}$ ____ = $\frac{\square}{\square}$

Unit: ____________________

I found this information on page ________.

Analyze *how to use the equation for average speed to find distance and time. Write the equation you could solve to find each.*

Distance: ____ = ____ Time: ____ = $\frac{\square}{\square}$

SUMMARIZE IT

Summarize two main ideas of the above sections.

____

____

____

Name ______________________ Date ____________

Main Idea **Details**

Velocity

I found this information on page ________.

Compare and contrast speed *and* velocity *by using the phrases listed to fill in the Venn diagram.*

- describes a rate
- includes direction
- is a vector
- describes how fast an object moves
- includes distance
- includes time
- is not a vector

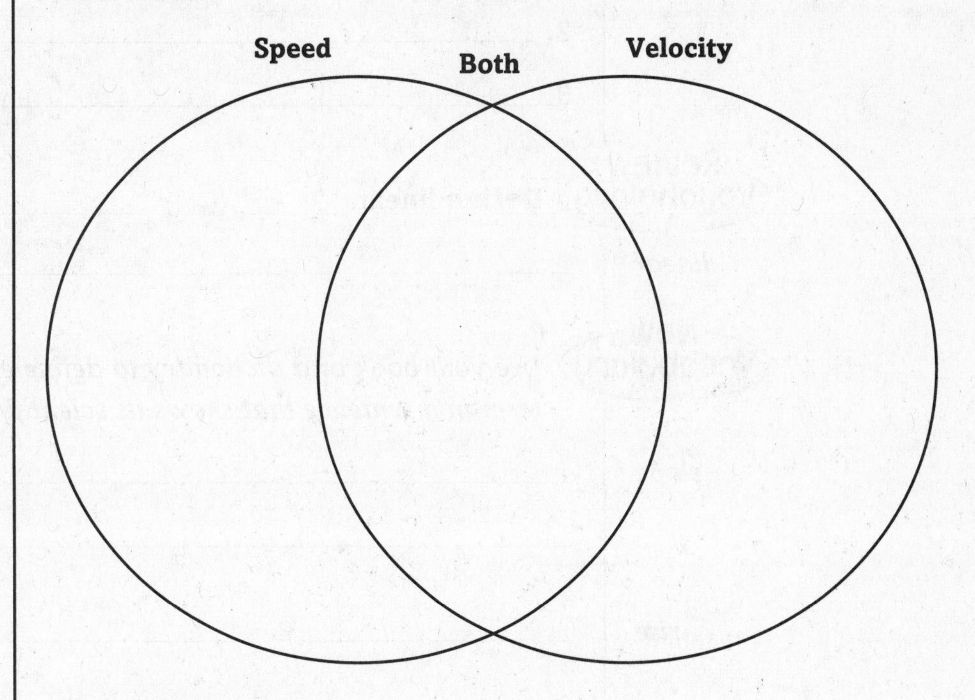

Acceleration

I found this information on page ________.

Distinguish *three ways that an object can accelerate. Complete the concept map.*

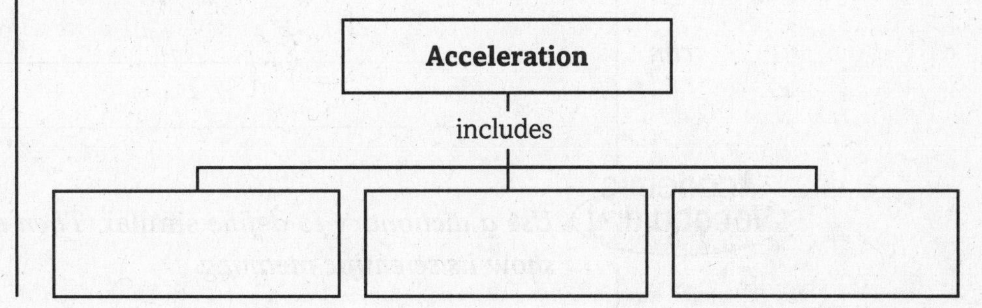

SUMMARIZE IT Summarize the main ideas of the above sections in two bullet points.

____

____

Name ______________________________ Date ____________

Motion

Lesson 3 Graphing Motion

Grade 8 Science Content Standards—1.f: Students know how to interpret graphs of position versus time and graphs of speed versus time for motion in a single direction. Also covers: 9.d, 9.e

Skim *Lesson 3 of your book. Write three questions that come to mind. Look for answers to your questions as you read the lesson.*

1. ______________________________

2. ______________________________

3. ______________________________

Review Vocabulary

Define linear.

linear ______________________________

New Vocabulary

Use your book or a dictionary to define each term. Then use the term in a sentence that shows its scientific meaning.

slope ______________________________

____

rise ______________________________

____

____

run ______________________________

____

Academic Vocabulary

Use a dictionary to define similar. *Then use it in a sentence to show its scientific meaning.*

similar ______________________________

____

Main Idea | **Details**

Position-Time Graphs

I found this information on page ________.

Create *a position-time graph. Use the data in the table in your book to sketch and label a graph.*

I found this information on page ________.

Complete *the sentence to show how* **speed is related to the slope of a position-time graph.**

The ______________ the slope of a position-time graph, the ______________ the speed.

I found this information on page ________.

Model *how to calculate the* **slope of a position-time graph.** *Label the* **rise** *and* **run** *on the graph below. Then write the* **equation for determining slope.**

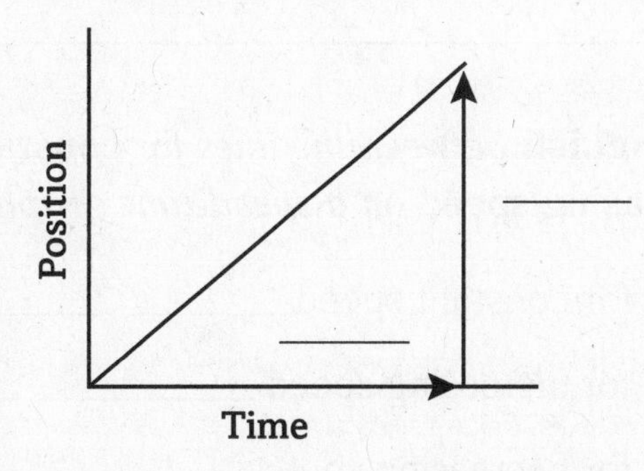

Slope = $\frac{\square}{\square}$

SUMMARIZE IT

Summarize two main ideas of the above section.

____

____

____

Name ______________________ Date __________

Main Idea	Details
Position-Time Graphs *I found this information on page ______.*	**Summarize** *the relationship between* **average speed** *and the* **slope of a position-time graph.** *Then explain how to find the average speed of an object with changing speed.* ______ ______ ______ ______
Speed-Time Graphs *I found this information on page ______.*	**Analyze** *the speed-time graph below. Label the axes and parts of the graph with the labels listed.* • Speed (m/s) • constant speed • increasing speed • Time (s) • decreasing speed

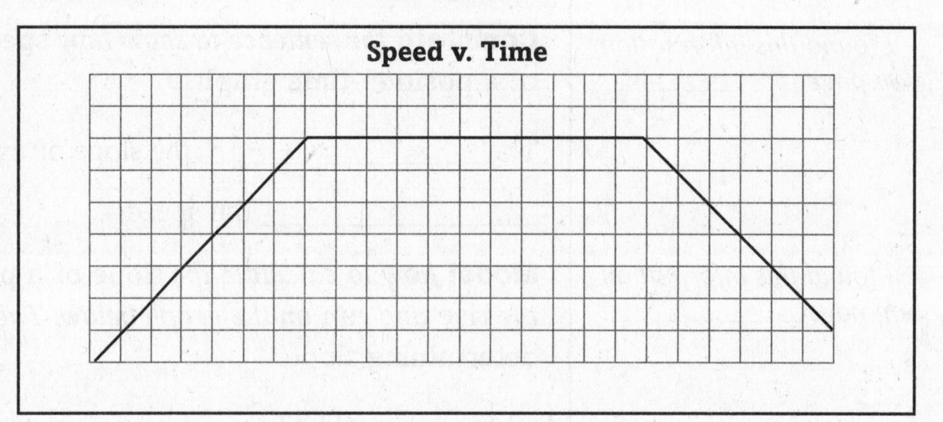

Main Idea	Details
I found this information on page ______.	**Distinguish** *between the lines for* **constant, increasing,** *and* **decreasing speed** *on a speed-time graph.* A line for constant speed ______. A line for increasing speed ______. A line for decreasing speed ______.

SUMMARIZE IT Summarize the main ideas of the above sections in two bullet points.

______

______

Name ______________________________ Date __________

Main Idea **Details**

Comparing Position-Time and Speed-Time Graphs

I found this information on page ________.

Create *drawings in the boxes provided to contrast the four types of motion described.*

Type of Motion	Position-Time Graph	Speed-Time Graph
Object at rest		
Object moving at constant speed		
Object speeding up		
Object slowing down		

SUMMARIZE IT Summarize two main ideas of the above section.

____

____

Name ______________________ Date __________

Motion Chapter Wrap-Up

Review the ideas you listed in the table at the beginning of the chapter. Cross out any incorrect information in the first column. Then complete the table by filling in the third column.

K What I know	W What I want to find out	L What I learned

Review

Use this checklist to help you study.

- ☐ Review the information you included in your Foldable.
- ☐ Study your *Science Notebook* on this chapter.
- ☐ Study the definitions of vocabulary words.
- ☐ Review daily homework assignments.
- ☐ Re-read the chapter and review the charts, graphs, and illustrations.
- ☐ Review the Standards Check at the end of each lesson.
- ☐ Look over the Standards Review at the end of the chapter.

SUMMARIZE IT **After studying the chapter, write one summary sentence for each lesson to illustrate the chapter's main ideas.**

____

____

____

Name ________________________________ Date ____________

Forces

Grade 8 Science Content Standards—2.c: Students know when the forces on an object are balanced, the motion of the object does not change. Also covers: 2.a, 2.b, 2.d, 2.e, 2.f

Before You Read

Before you read the chapter, think about what you know about the topic. List three things that you already know about forces in the first column. Then list three things that you would like to learn about forces in the second column.

K What I know	W What I want to find out

Construct the Foldable as directed at the beginning of this chapter.

Science Journal

Describe three examples of pushing or pulling on an object. In each case, how did the object move?

Name ______________________ Date __________

Forces

Lesson 1 Combining Forces

Grade 8 Science Content Standards—2.b: Students know when an object is subject to two or more forces at once, the result is the cumulative effect of all the forces. Also covers: 2.a, 2.c

Scan *Lesson 1 of your book. Read the headings, and look at the illustrations. Predict three things that will be discussed.*

1. ______________________

2. ______________________

3. ______________________

Review Vocabulary

Define vector *using your book or a dictionary.*

vector ______________________

New Vocabulary

Read the definitions below. Write the correct vocabulary term on the blank to the left of each definition.

__________ force that is exerted only when two objects are touching

__________ idea stating that when the net force acting on an object is zero, an object at rest remains at rest, and that when the object is moving, it continues to move in a straight line with constant speed

__________ push or pull

__________ combination of all of the forces acting on an object

__________ state in which the net force acting on an object is not zero

__________ state in which the net forces acting on an object are zero

__________ force that one object exerts on another when the objects are not touching

Academic Vocabulary

Use a dictionary to define specify. *Then use it in a sentence to show its scientific meaning.*

specify ______________________

____

Name ______________________________ Date __________

Main Idea — **Details**

What is a force?

I found this information on page ________.

Organize *information about* contact forces *and* noncontact forces *by completing the diagram.*

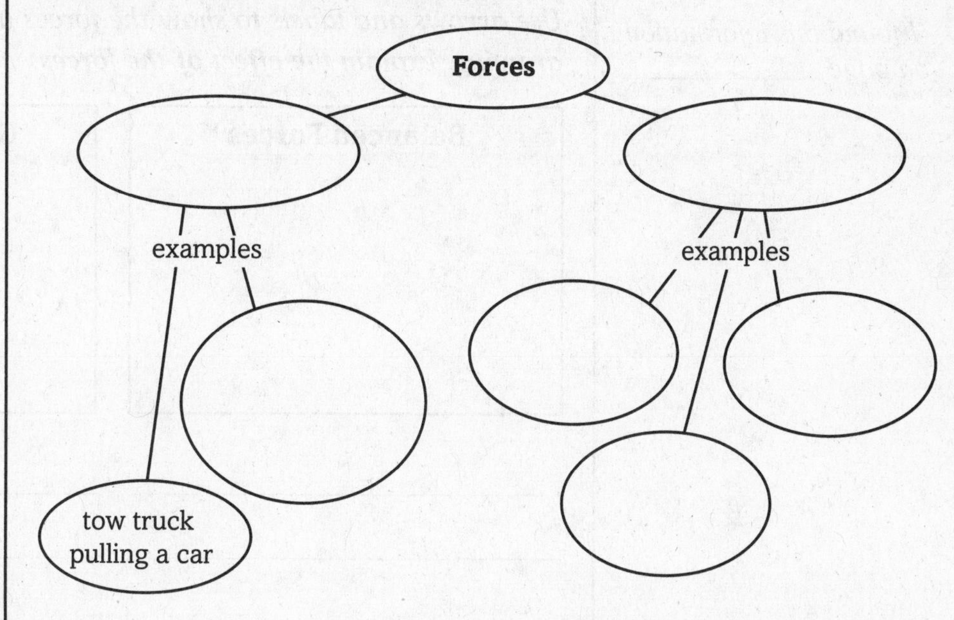

Combining Forces

I found this information on page ________.

Model *force vector arrows to show the* net forces *that result when each pair of forces is combined. Label the* magnitude *of each net force.*

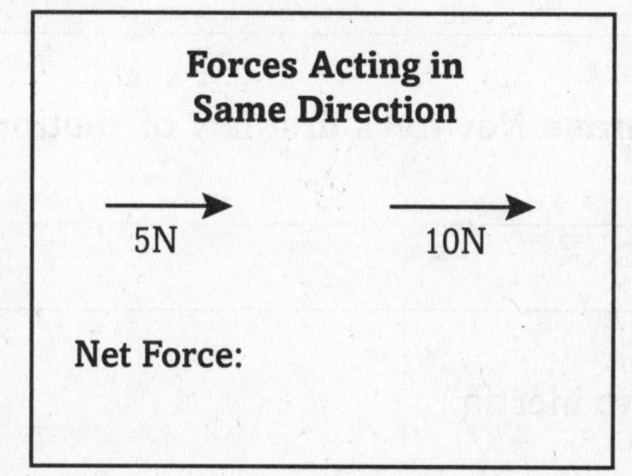

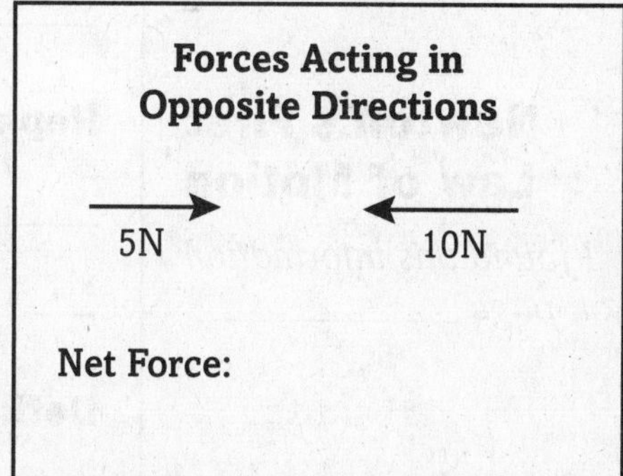

SUMMARIZE IT Summarize three main ideas of the above sections.

____

____

____

____

Name ______________________ Date __________

Main Idea | **Details**

How do forces affect motion?

I found this information on page ______.

Create *two drawings to show how an object is affected by* balanced *and* unbalanced *forces moving in opposite directions. Use arrows and labels to show the forces and motions. Below each drawing, explain the effect of the forces.*

Balanced Forces	Unbalanced Forces

Newton's First Law of Motion

I found this information on page ______.

Rephrase Newton's first law of motion *in your own words.*

____

____

Define inertia.

Inertia is ______________________________.

SUMMARIZE IT Summarize the main ideas of the above sections with two bullet points.

____

____

____

Name ______________________ Date ____________

Forces

Lesson 2 Types of Forces

Grade 8 Science Content Standards—2.d: Students know how to identify separately the two or more forces that are acting on a single static object, including gravity, elastic forces due to tension or compression in matter, and friction.

Scan *the* What You'll Learn *statements for Lesson 2 of your book. Identify three topics that will be discussed.*

1. ______________________
2. ______________________
3. ______________________

Review Vocabulary **Define** velocity, *using your book or a dictionary.*

velocity ______________________

New Vocabulary *Use your book to define the following terms.*

gravity ______________________

weight ______________________

friction ______________________

elastic force ______________________

tension force ______________________

compression force ______________________

normal force ______________________

Academic Vocabulary *Use a dictionary to define* involve.

involve ______________________

____

Name ______________________ Date __________

Main Idea | **Details**

What is gravity?

I found this information on page ______.

Rephrase *the* law of universal gravitation.

____

____

____

____

I found this information on page ______.

Label *the diagrams to indicate how a* change in distance or mass affects the gravitational attraction *between objects.*

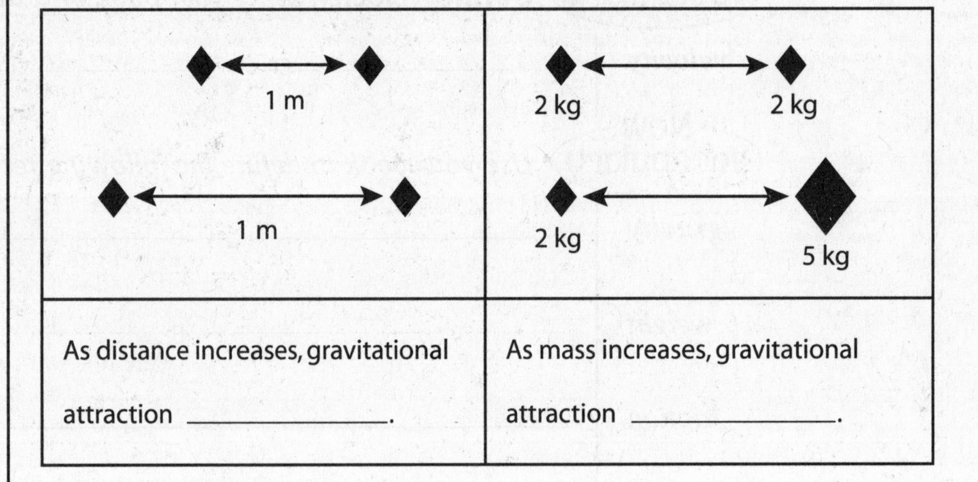

SUMMARIZE IT Summarize the main ideas of the above sections with two bullet points.

____

____

____

____

Name ______________________ Date __________

Main Idea | **Details**

Friction

I found this information on page ______.

Organize *information about* friction *by completing the table.*

Type of Friction	Definition	Example
Static		
Sliding		

Elastic Forces

I found this information on page ______.

Distinguish *between the two types of forces that produce* elastic forces *by completing the graphic organizer.*

Elastic Forces

are produced by

______	______
which is a	which is a
______	______
exerted when a material is	exerted when a material is
______	______

SUMMARIZE IT Summarize two main ideas of the above sections.

____

____

Name ______________________________ Date ____________

Main Idea | **Details**

Elastic Forces

I found this information on page ______.

Create *a drawing showing the forces acting on a cup resting on a table. Use arrows to show the directions in which the forces act. Label each arrow with the force it represents.*

Identifying Forces on an Object

I found this information on page ______.

For a book sliding on a table, **classify** *forces that act in the* horizontal direction *and forces that act in the* vertical direction *by completing the graphic organizer.*

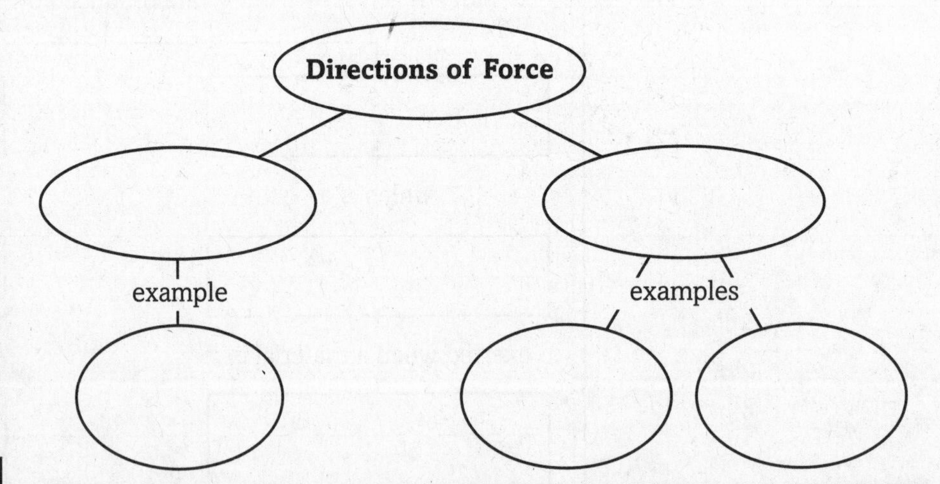

SUMMARIZE IT

Summarize two main ideas of the above sections.

Name ______________________ Date ____________

Forces

Lesson 3 Unbalanced Forces and Acceleration

Grade 8 Science Content Standards—2.e: Students know that when the forces on an object are unbalanced, the object will change its velocity (this is, it will speed up, slow down, or change direction). Also covers: 2.f

Scan *Lesson 3 of your book. Use the checklist below.*

- ☐ Read all of the headings.
- ☐ Read all of the bold words.
- ☐ Look at the pictures and tables.
- ☐ Think about what you already know about unbalanced forces and acceleration.

Write two things that you will learn about unbalanced forces and acceleration.

1. ______________________

2. ______________________

Review Vocabulary **Define** acceleration, *using your book or a dictionary.*

acceleration ______________________

New Vocabulary *Use your book or a dictionary to define the vocabulary terms.*

centripetal force ______________________

Newton's second law of motion ______________________

Newton's third law of motion ______________________

Name ____________________ Date ____________

Main Idea | **Details**

Unbalanced Forces and Velocity

I found this information on page ______.

Analyze *how* unbalanced forces change *the* velocity *and* acceleration *of objects by completing the cause-and-effect graphic organizers below.*

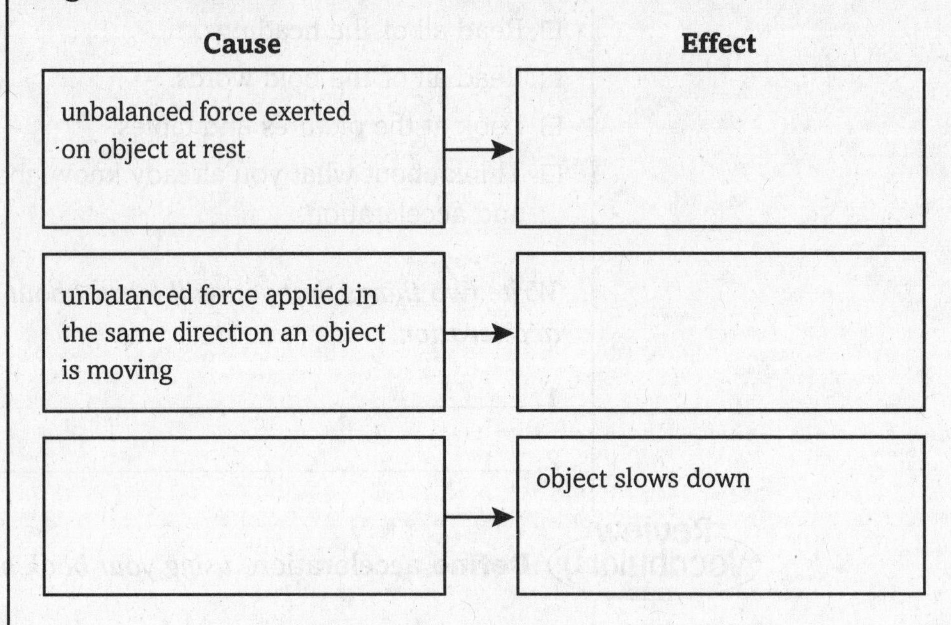

I found this information on page ______.

Create *a top view of an object moving in a circle at constant speed, such as a ball on a string. Show at least two positions of the object. At each position, draw an arrow for the object's velocity and another arrow for the centripetal force of the object.*

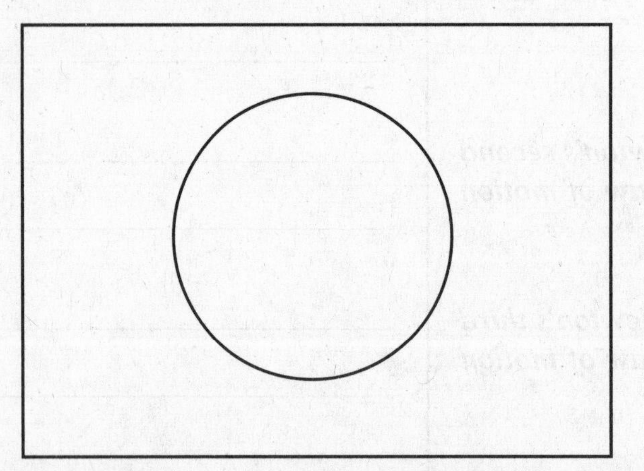

SUMMARIZE IT Summarize a main idea of the above section.

Name ______________________ Date __________

Main Idea	Details

Newton's Second Law of Motion

I found this information on page ________.

Complete *the concept map with properties of an object that are related by Newton's second law of motion.*

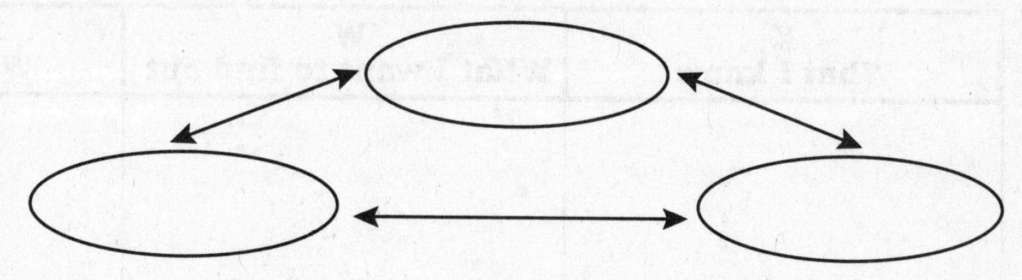

I found this information on page ________.

Define *how to* calculate average acceleration using Newton's second law of motion. *Complete the formula and the chart below.*

acceleration = ____________

= $\frac{F}{\_\_\_}$

Calculating Acceleration

Symbol	Stands for	Measured in
a		
	net force	newtons; N
		kilograms; kg

Newton's Third Law of Motion

I found this information on page ________.

Identify *the two forces involved in a force pair.*

____

____

SUMMARIZE IT Summarize a main idea from the above section.

____

____

____

Name ______________________________ Date ____________

Forces Chapter Wrap-Up

Review the ideas you listed in the table at the beginning of the chapter. Cross out any incorrect information in the first column. Then complete the table by filling in the third column.

K What I know	W What I want to find out	L What I learned

Review

Use this checklist to help you study.

- ☐ Review the information you included in your Foldable.
- ☐ Study your *Science Notebook* on this chapter.
- ☐ Study the definitions of vocabulary words.
- ☐ Review daily homework assignments.
- ☐ Re-read the chapter and review the tables and illustrations.
- ☐ Review the Standards Check at the end of each lesson.
- ☐ Look over the Standards Review at the end of the chapter.

SUMMARIZE IT

After studying the chapter, write one summary sentence for each lesson to illustrate the chapter's main ideas.

____

____

____

____

Name ______________________ Date __________

Density and Buoyancy

Grade 8 Science Content Standards—8.a: Students know density is mass per unit volume. Also covers: 8.b, 8.c, 8.d, 9.f

Before You Read

Before you read the chapter, think about what you know about the topic. List three things that you already know about density and buoyancy in the first column. Then list three things that you would like to learn about them in the second column.

K What I know	W What I want to find out

FOLDABLES™ Study Organizer

Construct the Foldable as directed at the beginning of this chapter.

Science Journal

Compare and contrast three objects that float with three objects that sink.

Name ____________________ Date ____________

Density and Buoyancy

Lesson 1 Density

Grade 8 Science Content Standards—8.a: Students know density is mass per unit volume. Also covers: 8.b, 9.f

Scan *Lesson 1 of your book. Use the checklist below.*

- ☐ Read all of the headings.
- ☐ Read all of the bold words.
- ☐ Look at the tables and pictures.
- ☐ Think about what you already know about density.

Write three facts that you discovered.

1. ____________________

2. ____________________

3. ____________________

Review Vocabulary

Define volume *using your book or a dictionary.*

volume ____________________

New Vocabulary

Use your book or a dictionary to define the vocabulary terms. Then use each term in a sentence that shows its scientific meaning.

density ____________________

rectangular solid ____________________

Academic Vocabulary

Define preceding.

preceding ____________________

Name ______________________________ Date ____________

Main Idea | **Details**

What is density?

I found this information on page ______.

Draw *and label an arrow to show how* density *changes as the* mass *and* number of particles *in an equal volume change.*

less mass → more mass

fewer particles → more particles

I found this information on page ______.

Complete *the equation with words to show* how density is calculated. *Give the unit for each part of the equation. Then write the equation with symbols.*

density (__________) = ______________ divided by ______________

Equation: ______________

I found this information on page ______.

Summarize *the two properties that change when a material is broken into smaller pieces and the one that does not.*

The ______________ and ______________ of the material change,

but its ______________ does not change.

I found this information on page ______.

Analyze *the factors that determine the density of a material. Complete the diagram.*

The density of a material depends on ______________ / ______________

SUMMARIZE IT Summarize the main ideas of the above section in two bullet points.

____

____

____

Name ______________________ Date __________

Main Idea | **Details**

Measuring Density

I found this information on page ______.

Summarize *the steps used to find* the density of a liquid.

1. ______________________
2. ______________________
3. ______________________

I found this information on page ______.

Complete *the formula below to show how to calculate* the volume of a rectangular solid.

Volume = ________ × ________ × ________

I found this information on page ______.

Sequence *the steps used to find* the volume of an irregular solid. *Draw how the lab equipment might look for each step.*

1. Place water in a graduated cylinder, and record its volume.

↓

2.

↓

3.

SUMMARIZE IT

Summarize two main ideas of the above section.

____

____

____

____

Name ______________________ Date __________

Density and Buoyancy

Lesson 2 Pressure and the Buoyant Force

Grade 8 Science Content Standards—8.c: Students know the buoyant force on an object in a fluid is an upward force equal to the weight of the fluid the object has displaced. Also covers: 9.f

Scan *the headings in Lesson 2 of your book. Predict three topics that will be discussed.*

1. ______________________
2. ______________________
3. ______________________

Review Vocabulary

Define force *using your book or a dictionary.*

force ______________________

New Vocabulary

Use your book or a dictionary to define the vocabulary terms. Then use each term in a sentence to show its scientific meaning.

fluid ______________________

____

pressure ______________________

____

atmospheric pressure ______________________

____

buoyant force ______________________

____

Academic Vocabulary

Use a dictionary to define area *to show its scientific meaning.*

area ______________________

Name ______________________ Date ____________

Main Idea | **Details**

Pressure in a Fluid

I found this information on page ________.

Classify *the 2 types of* fluids, *and give an example of each.*

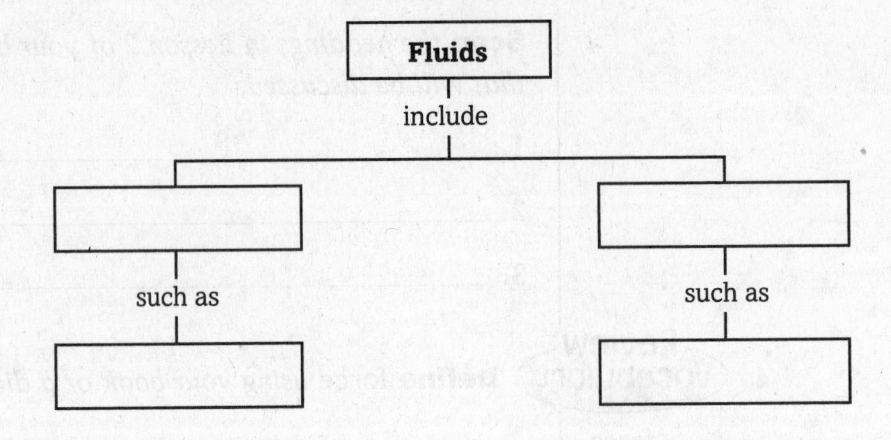

I found this information on page ________.

Summarize *the* effects of force and area on pressure *by completing the diagram.*

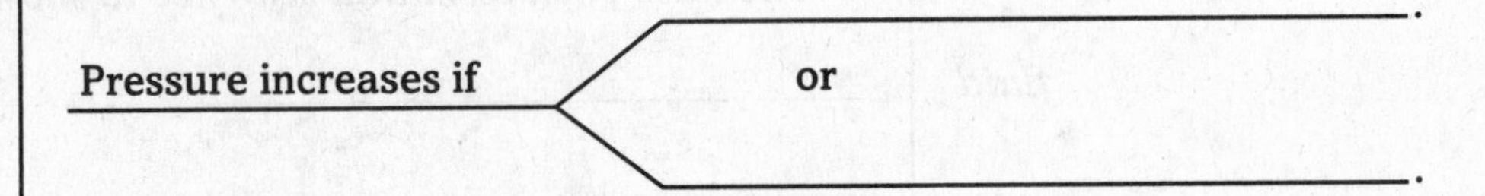

I found this information on page ________.

Sequence *the diagrams to show how pressure is related to surface area. Number the diagrams from 1 (least pressure) to 3 (most pressure).*

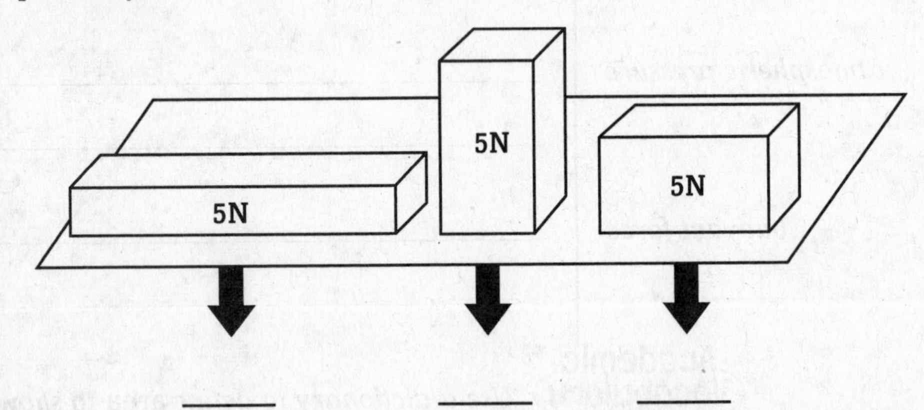

SUMMARIZE IT Rephrase two main ideas of the above section.

Name ______________________________ Date ____________

Main Idea | **Details**

Pressure in a Fluid

I found this information on page ________.

Complete *the equation for* calculating pressure. *Include the units used for each measurement. Then write the equation in symbols.*

Pressure (in __________) = __________ (in __________) / __________ (in meters squared)

I found this information on page ________.

Analyze ***how the pressure exerted by a fluid changes with height and depth.***

As the height of a column of fluid increases, ______________________________.

As the depth below the surface of a fluid increases, ______________________________.

I found this information on page ________.

Model ***the effect of pressure on a fluid at different levels. Indicate the force with which milk would squirt out of holes punched in the side of the milk carton.***

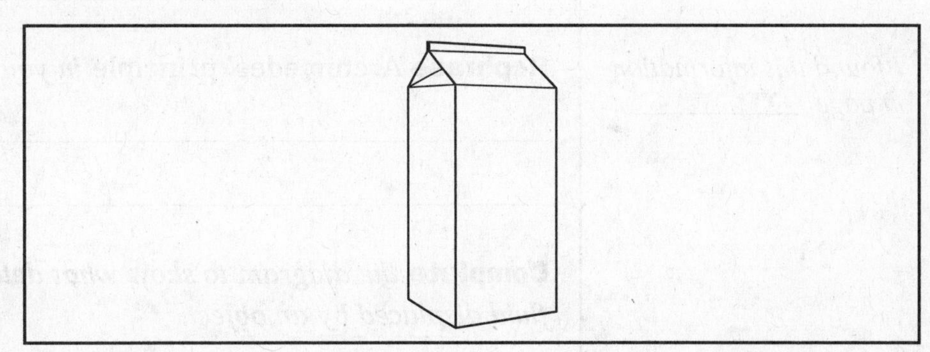

I found this information on page ________.

Summarize *how* atmospheric pressure *changes as* elevation *changes.*

Higher elevation → __________ atmospheric pressure

SUMMARIZE IT Summarize three main ideas of the above section.

____

____

____

Name ______________________ Date __________

Main Idea | **Details**

What causes the buoyant force?

I found this information on page ______.

Model *the* buoyant force *on an object. Draw a fish under water. Use arrows to show the forces acting on the fish. Then write a sentence explaining why the net force is upward.*

____

I found this information on page ______.

Rephrase Archimedes' principle *in your own words.*

____

____

Complete *the diagram to show what determines the weight of the fluid displaced by an object.*

The weight of the displaced fluid depends on
- ______________________________
- ______________________________

SUMMARIZE IT Choose two main ideas from this section.

____

____

____

Name ____________________ Date __________

Density and Buoyancy

Lesson 3 Sinking and Floating

Grade 8 Science Content Standards—8.d: Students know how to predict whether an object will float or sink.

Skim *Lesson 3 of your book. Write three questions that come to mind. Look for answers to your questions as you read the lesson.*

1. ____________________
2. ____________________
3. ____________________

Review Vocabulary

Define gravity *using your book or a dictionary, then write a sentence to show its scientific meaning.*

gravity ____________________

New Vocabulary

Use your book or a dictionary to define the vocabulary term. Then use the term in a sentence that shows its scientific meaning.

hydrometer ____________________

Academic Vocabulary

Use your book or a dictionary to define ratio, *then use it in a sentence to show its scientific meaning.*

ratio ____________________

Main Idea	Details

Why do objects sink or float?

I found this information on page ______.

Analyze *what causes an object to* sink *or* float. *Complete the cause-and-effect diagrams.*

Upward buoyant force is greater than object's weight. → ______

Upward buoyant force is less than object's weight. → ______

The Buoyant Force and Density

I found this information on page ______.

Organize *information about the relationship between the* density of an object *and* its ability to sink or float *by completing the table.*

If the density of an object is . . .	Then it will . . .
Less than the density of a fluid	
Greater than the density of a fluid	

I found this information on page ______.

Summarize *the reason that a metal boat floats even though the metal's density is greater than that of water.*

______

______

______

Identify *the* function of a hydrometer.

A hydrometer is used to ______.

SUMMARIZE IT

Summarize two main ideas of the above sections.

______

______

______

______

Main Idea | **Details**

The Buoyant Force and Density

I found this information on page ________.

Model *how a hydrometer floats in* a liquid more dense than water *and in* a liquid less dense than water. *Draw the hydrometer's position in each diagram.*

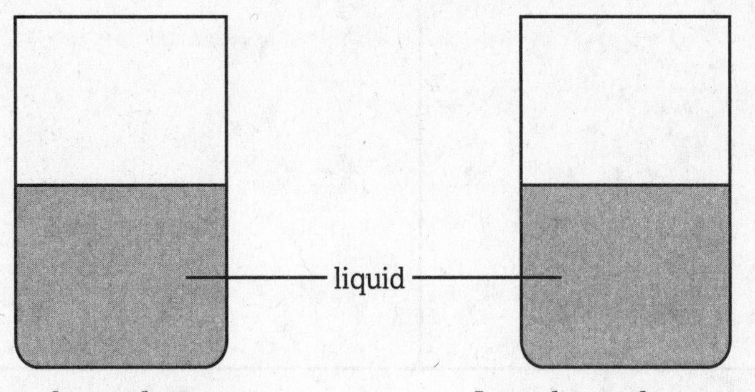

Floating and Sinking in the Atmosphere

I found this information on page ________.

Compare and contrast *helium and hot-air balloons. Complete the Venn diagram with at least five facts.*

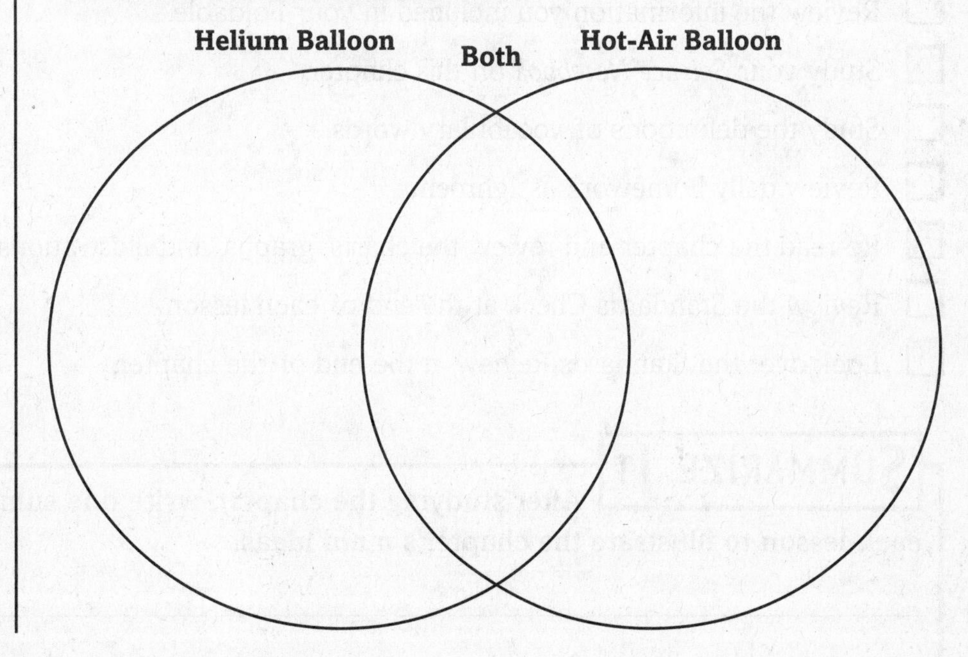

SUMMARIZE IT Rephrase the main ideas of the above sections.

____

____

Name ______________________________ Date __________

Density and Buoyancy Chapter Wrap-Up

Review the ideas you listed in the table at the beginning of the chapter. Cross out any incorrect information in the first column. Then complete the table by filling in the third column.

K What I know	W What I want to find out	L What I learned

Review

Use this checklist to help you study.

- ☐ Review the information you included in your Foldable.
- ☐ Study your *Science Notebook* on this chapter.
- ☐ Study the definitions of vocabulary words.
- ☐ Review daily homework assignments.
- ☐ Re-read the chapter and review the charts, graphs, and illustrations.
- ☐ Review the Standards Check at the end of each lesson.
- ☐ Look over the Standards Review at the end of the chapter.

SUMMARIZE IT **After studying the chapter, write one summary sentence for each lesson to illustrate the chapter's main ideas.**

____

____

____

____

____

Name ______________________________ Date __________

Understanding the Atom

Grade 8 Science Content Standards—3.a: Students know the structure of the atom and know it is composed of protons, neutrons, and electrons. Also covers: 3.f, 7.b

Before You Read

Before you read the chapter, think about what you know about the topic. List three things that you already know about atoms in the first column. Then list three things that you would like to learn about atoms in the second column.

K What I know	W What I want to find out

Construct the Foldable as directed at the beginning of this chapter.

Science Journal

Write a paragraph on what you know about the atom.

Name ______________________ Date ______________

Understanding the Atom

Lesson 1 Atoms—Basic Units of Matter

Grade 8 Science Content Standards—3.a: Students know the structure of the atom and know it is composed of protons, neutrons, and electrons.

Scan *the* What You'll Learn *statements for Lesson 1. List three topics that will be discussed.*

1. ______________________

2. ______________________

3. ______________________

Review Vocabulary

Define mass *using your book or a dictionary.*

mass ______________________

____

New Vocabulary

Write a paragraph using all of the vocabulary terms to show their meanings.

matter
atom
nucleus
proton
neutron
electron

____

Academic Vocabulary

Use your book or a dictionary to define proportion. *Then use the term in a sentence.*

proportion ______________________

____

Name ______________________ Date ____________

Main Idea | **Details**

What is the current atomic model?

I found this information on page ________.

Conclude *why the* atomic-force microscope *is important to scientists.*

____

____

Compare protons, neutrons, *and* electrons.

Particle	Where Found	Charge	Mass (amu)
Proton		+1	
Neutron			1.008701
Electron			

Is there historical evidence of atoms?

I found this information on page ________.

Organize *information about* Democritus's theory of the atom *using the concept map.*

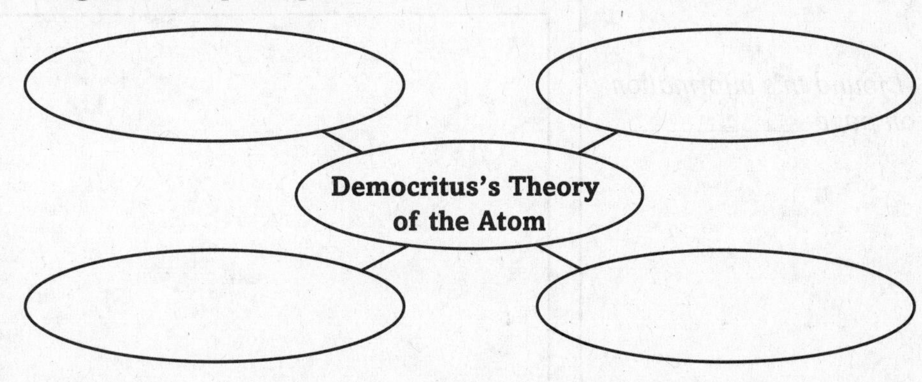

Complete *the statement to summarize* what an atom is.

An atom of aluminum is ______________________.

SUMMARIZE IT

Summarize three main ideas from the above sections.

____

____

____

Main Idea | **Details**

Is there historical evidence of atoms?

I found this information on page ________.

Sequence *the steps of* Antoine Lavoisier's experiments *on mercury (II) oxide. Complete the flow chart.*

Summarize *the* law of conservation of mass *and the* law of definite proportions.

Law of Conservation of Mass: ____________________

____

Law of Definite Proportions: ____________________

____

Create *a concept map for the* 5 principles of Dalton's atomic model.

I found this information on page ________.

SUMMARIZE IT

Summarize three main ideas of the above sections.

____

____

____

____

Name ______________________ Date __________

Understanding the Atom

Lesson 2 Discovering Parts of the Atom

Grade 8 Science Content Standards—3.a: Students know the structure of the atom and know it is composed of protons, neutrons, and electrons.

Skim *Lesson 2 of your book. Write three questions that come to mind. Look for answers to your questions as you read the lesson.*

1. ______________________
2. ______________________
3. ______________________

Review Vocabulary

Define electromagnetic spectrum *using your book or a dictionary.*

electromagnetic spectrum ______________________

New Vocabulary

Use your book or a dictionary to define each term. Then use each term in a sentence that shows its scientific meaning.

spectral line ______________________

energy level ______________________

electron cloud ______________________

Academic Vocabulary

Use a dictionary to define research.

research ______________________

Name ______________________________ Date ____________

Main Idea | **Details**

How were electrons discovered?

I found this information on page ______.

Model *Thomson's* cathode-ray tube experiment. *Draw a diagram showing the experiment.*

Summarize *three conclusions Thomson drew from his experiments.*

1. ______________________________

2. ______________________________

3. ______________________________

Rutherford—Discovering the Nucleus

I found this information on page ______.

Contrast *the* predicted *and* actual *outcomes of Rutherford's students'* gold-foil experiment.

Predicted Outcome	Actual Outcome

SUMMARIZE IT Summarize two main ideas from the above sections.

____

Name ______________________________ Date ______________

Main Idea | **Details**

Rutherford—Discovering the Nucleus

I found this information on page ______.

Create *a drawing showing* Rutherford's model of the atom. *Label the* nucleus *and* electrons.

Bohr and the Hydrogen Atom.

I found this information on page ______.

Contrast *the* Bohr model *and the* Rutherford model *of how electrons move in an atom.*

____

____

____

I found this information on page ______.

Analyze *how* spectral lines *are related to* energy levels. *Complete the statements.*

When an electron falls from a higher energy level to a lower one, it ______________ energy. This produces ______________.

SUMMARIZE IT

Summarize two main ideas from the above sections.

____

____

____

Name ______________________________ Date ______________

Main Idea	Details
Bohr and the Hydrogen Atom *I found this information on page* ________.	**Model** *the* Bohr atom. *Draw an atom including 2* energy levels. *Show how many electrons can fit in each energy level.*
I found this information on page ________.	**Analyze** *the strengths and weaknesses of the* Bohr model of the atom. The Bohr model explained ______________________ ______________. It did not explain ______________________ ______________________________________.
The Electron Cloud *I found this information on page* ________.	**Contrast** *the* electron cloud model *with the* Bohr model *of the atom.* ______________________________________ ______________________________________ ______________________________________

SUMMARIZE IT

Summarize the main ideas of the above sections of this lesson with three bullet points.

____

____

____

____

Name ______________________ Date __________

Understanding the Atom

Lesson 3 Elements, Isotopes, and Ions—How Atoms Differ

Grade 8 Science Content Standards—3.f: Students know how to use the periodic table to indentify elements in simple compounds. Also covers: 7.b

Scan *Lesson 3 of your book. Read the headings and look at the illustrations. Predict three topics that will be discussed.*

1. ______________________

2. ______________________

3. ______________________

Review Vocabulary

Define periodic table *using your book or a dictionary.*

periodic table ______________________

New Vocabulary

Read the definitions below. Write the correct vocabulary term on the blank to the left of each definition.

__________ total mass of an atom

__________ pure substance made from atoms that all have the same number of protons

__________ number of protons in an atom of an element

__________ atom that has gained or lost electrons and is no longer neutral

__________ sum of the number of protons and neutrons that an atom has

__________ atoms of the same element that have different numbers of neutrons

Academic Vocabulary

Use your book or a dictionary to define **contrast.**

contrast ______________________

Name ______________________________ Date ______________

Main Idea | **Details**

Different Elements—Different Numbers of Protons

I found this information on page ________.

Sequence *the elements* gold, copper, *and* sulfur *in order by the number of protons in their nuclei. Write the* atomic number *for each element.*

1. Element: ______________ Atomic number: ________
2. Element: ______________ Atomic number: ________
3. Element: ______________ Atomic number: ________

Atomic Number and the Periodic Table

I found this information on page ________.

Model *the periodic table. Shade the* metals, nonmetals, *and* metalloids. *Then draw and label an arrow to show how* atomic number *changes as you move across a row of the table.*

Periodic Table of Elements

	1	2	3	4	5	6	7	8	9	10	11	12	13	14	15	16	17	18
1	1 H																	2 He
2	3 Li	4 Be											5 B	6 C	7 N	8 O	9 F	10 Ne
3	11 Na	12 Mg											13 Al	14 Si	15 P	16 S	17 Cl	18 Ar
4	19 K	20 Ca	21 Sc	22 Ti	23 V	24 Cr	25 Mn	26 Fe	27 Co	28 Ni	29 Cu	30 Zn	31 Ga	32 Ge	33 As	34 Se	35 Br	36 Kr
5	37 Rb	38 Sr	39 Y	40 Zr	41 Nb	42 Mo	43 Tc	44 Ru	45 Rh	46 Pd	47 Ag	48 Cd	49 In	50 Sn	51 Sb	52 Te	53 I	54 Xe
6	55 Cs	56 Ba	57 La*	72 Hf	73 Ta	74 W	75 Re	76 Os	77 Ir	78 Pt	79 Au	80 Hg	81 Tl	82 Pb	83 Bi	84 Po	85 At	86 Rn
7	87 Fr	88 Ra	89 Ac~	104 Rf	105 Db	106 Sg	107 Bh	108 Hs	109 Mt	110 Ds	111 Uuu	112 Uub		114 Uuq		116 Uuh		118 Uuo

58 Ce	59 Pr	60 Nd	61 Pm	62 Sm	63 Eu	64 Gd	65 Tb	66 Dy	67 Ho	68 Er	69 Tm	70 Yb	71 Lu
90 Th	91 Pa	92 U	93 Np	94 Pu	95 Am	96 Cm	97 Bk	98 Cf	99 Es	100 Fm	101 Md	102 No	103 Lr

Isotopes—Different Numbers of Neutrons

I found this information on page ________.

Create *a drawing showing two* isotopes *of neon with* mass numbers *of 20 and 22. Neon has an* atomic number *of 10.*

SUMMARIZE IT

Summarize two main ideas from the above sections.

____

____

Name ______________________________ Date __________

Main Idea — **Details**

Isotopes—Different Numbers of Neutrons

I found this information on page ________.

Summarize *uses of some* radioactive isotopes *in the concept map.*

Uses of Radioactive Isotopes

carbon-14	uranium-238	californium-252

I found this information on page ________.

Organize *information about the 3 main isotopes of hydrogen. List the* mass number *and* number of neutrons *for each. Put a check mark by the radioactive isotope.*

Protium: ______________________________

Deuterium: ______________________________

Tritium: ______________________________

Ions—Gaining or Losing Electrons

I found this information on page ________.

Contrast positive *and* negative ions. *Draw an example of each. Then complete the rest of the table.*

	Positive Ion	Negative Ion
Sketch		
Formed when		

SUMMARIZE IT Summarize the main ideas of the above sections.

____

____

____

Name ______________________ Date __________

Understanding the Atom

Chapter Wrap-Up

Review the ideas you listed in the table at the beginning of the chapter. Cross out any incorrect information in the first column. Then complete the table by filling in the third column.

K What I know	W What I want to find out	L What I learned

Review

Use this checklist to help you study.

- ☐ Review the information you included in your Foldable.
- ☐ Study your *Science Notebook* on this chapter.
- ☐ Study the definitions of vocabulary words.
- ☐ Review daily homework assignments.
- ☐ Re-read the chapter and review the charts, graphs, and illustrations.
- ☐ Review the Standards Check at the end of each lesson.
- ☐ Look over the Standards Review at the end of the chapter.

SUMMARIZE IT **After reading the chapter, write one or two sentences to summarize the main ideas of each section.**

____

____

____

Name ____________________ Date ____________

Combining Atoms and Molecules

Grade 8 Science Content Standards—3.a: Students know the structure of the atom and know it is composed of protons, neutrons, and electrons. Also covers: 3.b, 3.c, 3.f, 7.c

Before You Read

Before you read the chapter, respond to these statements.

1. Write an **A** if you agree with the statement.
2. Write a **D** if you disagree with the statement.

Before You Read	Combining Atoms and Molecules
	• The properties of a chemical compound are the same as the properties of each element it contains.
	• An atom that receives an electron becomes negatively charged.
	• Elements that are stable cannot form compounds..
	• Most elements are metals.

Construct the Foldable as directed at the beginning of this chapter.

Science Journal

Write three questions you have about solids.

Name ______________________ Date ____________

Combining Atoms and Molecules

Lesson 1 How Atoms Form Compounds

Grade 8 Science Content Standards—3.a: Students know the structure of the atom and know it is composed of protons, neutrons, and electrons. Also covers: 3.b, 3.f

Skim *Lesson 1 of your book. Predict four topics that might be discussed.*

1. ______________________
2. ______________________
3. ______________________
4. ______________________

Review Vocabulary

Define ion *using your book or a dictionary.*

ion ______________________

New Vocabulary

Use your book to define the following terms.

compound ______________________

chemical formula ______________________

molecule ______________________

chemical bond ______________________

ionic bond ______________________

valence ______________________

covalent bond ______________________

Academic Vocabulary

Use a dictionary to define symbol. *Then use it in a sentence to show its scientific meaning.*

symbol ______________________

____

Name ______________________________ Date ____________

Main Idea | **Details**

What is a compound?

I found this information on page ____________.

Contrast elements *with* compounds *by using the phrases to complete the Venn diagram.*

- made of more than one kind of atom
- about 100 kinds exist
- include water and table sugar
- include gold and carbon
- made of only one kind of atom
- can be described by a chemical formula

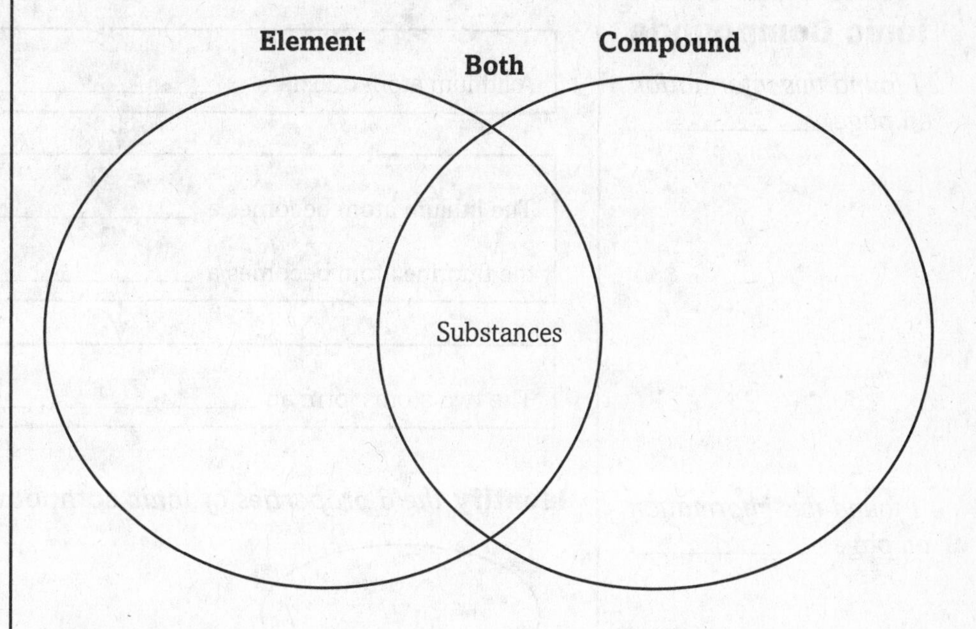

I found this information on page ____________.

Identify *two things a* chemical formula *tells you about a compound.*

H_2O_2

Chemical symbols indicate
____
____
________________________.

Subscript numbers indicate
____
____
________________________.

SUMMARIZE IT Summarize two main ideas of the above sections.

____
____
____

Name ______________________ Date __________

Main Idea | **Details**

What is a compound?

I found this information on page ________.

Distinguish *between the properties of the elements sodium and chlorine and the compound that they form.*

sodium + chlorine = sodium chloride

__________ __________ __________

Ionic Bonds and Ionic Compounds

I found this information on page ________.

Sequence *the steps in the formation of lithium fluoride.*

A lithium atom transfers ______________ to a fluorine atom.

↓

The lithium atom becomes a ______________, and the fluorine atom becomes a ______________.

↓

The two atoms form an ______________.

I found this information on page ________.

Identify *the 6 properties of ionic* compounds.

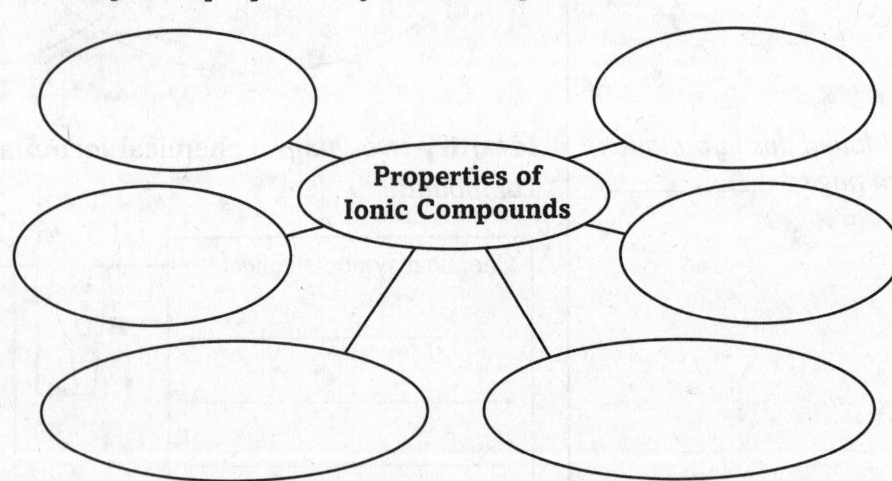

SUMMARIZE IT Summarize the main ideas of the above sections.

____

____

____

Name ______________________________ Date __________

Main Idea	Details

Ionic Bonds and Ionic Compounds

I found this information on page ________.

Summarize *what can be learned about an element from its* Lewis dot diagram.

____

____

Model *the arrangement of the valence electrons of different elements by constructing a Lewis dot diagram for each element below.*

Lithium	Beryllium	Boron	Carbon	Nitrogen	Oxygen	Fluorine	Neon

I found this information on page ________.

Define noble gas, *and explain why noble gases are stable.*

A noble gas is ______________________________

______________.

A noble gas is stable because ______________________________.

Covalent Bonds—Sharing Electrons

I found this information on page ________.

Identify *five properties of* covalent compounds.

1. ______________________________
2. ______________________________
3. ______________________________
4. ______________________________
5. ______________________________

SUMMARIZE IT Summarize the main ideas of the above sections in three bullet points.

____

____

____

Name ______________________ Date __________

Main Idea | **Details**

Covalent Bonds—Sharing Electrons

I found this information on page ______.

Organize *information about the* types of covalent bonds *by filling in the table below.*

Type of Covalent Bond	Description	Example
Single		H_2
Double		
Triple		

I found this information on page ______.

Compare and contrast ionic bonds *and* covalent bonds *by completing the Venn diagram below with at least six facts.*

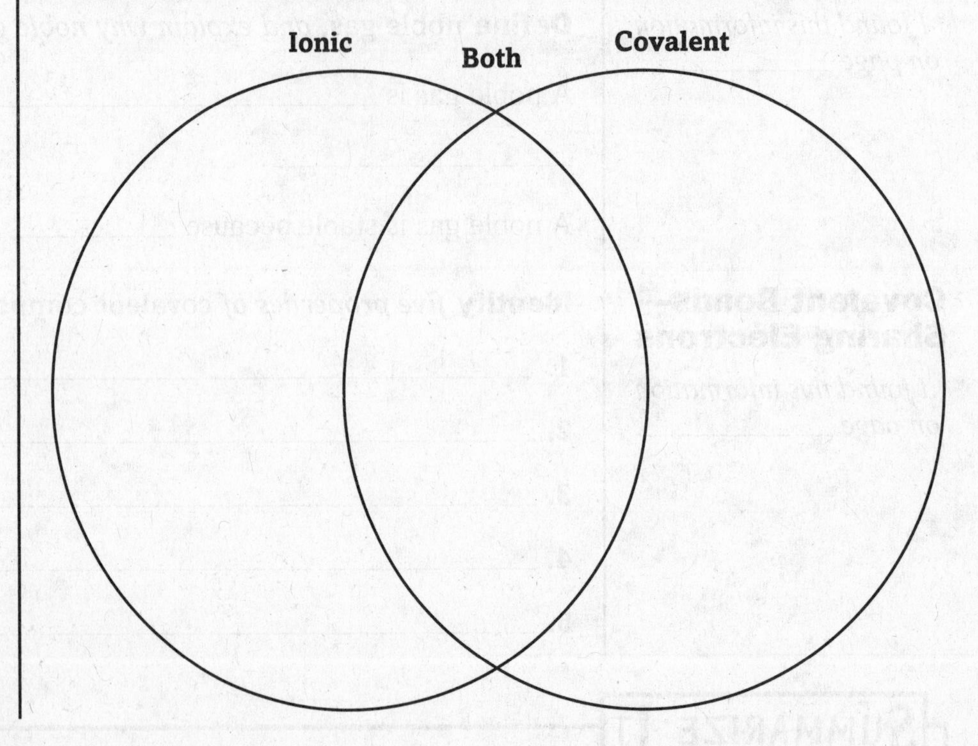

SUMMARIZE IT Summarize two main ideas about covalent bonds with two bullet points.

____

____

Name ______________________ Date __________

Combining Atoms and Molecules

Lesson 2 Forming Solids

Grade 8 Science Content Standards—3.c: Students know atoms and molecules form solids by building up repeating patterns, such as the crystal structure of NaCl or long-chain polymers. Also covers: 3.b, 7.c

Scan *Lesson 2 of your book. Predict three topics that might be discussed.*

1. ______________________

2. ______________________

3. ______________________

Review Vocabulary

Define element *using your book or a dictionary.*

element ______________________

____

New Vocabulary

Read the definitions below. Write the correct vocabulary term on the blank to the left of each definition.

__________ bond formed when many metal atoms share their pooled electrons

__________ ability of a substance to be pulled into wires

__________ ability of a material to be hammered or rolled into sheets

__________ regular, repeating arrangement of atoms, ions, or molecules

__________ element that is usually shiny, a good conductor of heat and electricity, and a solid at room temperature

__________ covalent compound made up of many small, repeating units linked together in a chain

__________ small molecule that forms a link in a polymer chain

Academic Vocabulary

Use a dictionary to define the verb alternate. *Then use it in a sentence.*

alternate ______________________

____

Name ______________________ Date __________

Main Idea — **Details**

Metals

I found this information on page ______.

Organize *information about* metals *in the table.*

Some Types of Metal	Examples of Uses
Gold	
Copper	
Aluminum	
Steel (iron)	

I found this information on page ______.

Create *a spider diagram that shows the 5 physical properties of metals.*

Crystals

I found this information on page ______.

Distinguish *between the types of bonds that can form crystals.*

Bonds That Can Form Crystals	
Type of Bond	Example of Crystal
	sodium chloride

SUMMARIZE IT Summarize two of the main points of the above sections.

____

____

Name ______________________________ Date ____________

Main Idea | **Details**

Crystals

I found this information on page ________.

Model *the* unit cell *for sodium chloride and quartz in the spaces below.*

Sodium Chloride	Quartz

What is a polymer?

I found this information on page ________.

Complete *the paragraph below about* polymers.

A ____________ is a covalent compound made of many small, repeating units linked together in a ____________. The word polymer means ____________. A ____________ is a small molecule that forms a link in a polymer chain. The monomer ____________ links together to form polyethylene.

I found this information on page ________.

Classify *the examples of* polymers *in the table as synthetic or natural, and name the* monomer *that makes up each.*

Example	Type of Polymer	Monomer
Polyethylene		ethene
DNA		
Protein		
Carbohydrate		

SUMMARIZE IT **Highlight the main idea of this section below.**

Polymers are covalent compounds made up of repeating monomers. Polymers can be synthetic or natural. Examples of polymers include polyethylene, DNA, and carbohydrates.

Name ______________________ Date __________

Combining Atoms and Molecules

Chapter Wrap-Up

Now that you have read the chapter, think about what you have learned and complete the table below. Compare your previous answers to these.

1. Write an **A** if you agree with the statement.
2. Write a **D** if you disagree with the statement.

Combining Atoms and Molecules	After You Read
• The properties of a chemical compound are the same as the properties of each element it contains.	
• An atom that receives an electron becomes negatively charged.	
• Elements that are stable rarely form compounds.	
• Most elements are metals.	

Review

Use this checklist to help you study.

- ☐ Review the information you included in your Foldable.
- ☐ Study your *Science Notebook* on this chapter.
- ☐ Study the definitions of vocabulary words.
- ☐ Review daily homework assignments.
- ☐ Re-read the chapter and review the charts, graphs, and illustrations.
- ☐ Review the Standards Check at the end of each lesson.
- ☐ Look over the Standards Review at the end of the chapter.

SUMMARIZE IT **After studying the chapter, list three key concepts you have learned about chemical bonds.**

____

____

____

Name ______________________________ Date ____________

States of Matter

Grade 8 Science Content Standards—3.e: Students know that in solids the atoms are closely locked in position and can only vibrate; in liquids the atoms and molecules are more loosely connected and can collide with and move past one another; and in gases the atoms and molecules are free to move independently, colliding frequently. Also covers: 3.d, 5.d

Before You Read

Before you read the chapter, think about what you know about the topic. List three things that you already know about states of matter in the first column. Then list three things that you would like to learn about states of matter in the second column.

K What I know	W What I want to find out

FOLDABLES™ Study Organizer

Construct the Foldable as directed at the beginning of this chapter.

Science Journal

List three differences between ice and water.

Name ______________________ Date __________

States of Matter

Lesson 1 Solids, Liquids, and Gases

Grade 8 Science Content Standards—3.e: Students know that in solids the atoms are closely locked in position and can only vibrate; in liquids the atoms and molecules are more loosely connected and can collide with and move past one another; and in gases the atoms and molecules are free to move independently, colliding frequently. Also covers: 3.d

Scan *Lesson 1 of your book. Use the checklist below.*

- ☐ Read all the headings.
- ☐ Read all the bold words.
- ☐ Look at the charts and pictures.
- ☐ Think about what you already know about states of matter.

Write three things that you learn about states of matter.

1. ______________________
2. ______________________
3. ______________________

Review Vocabulary

Define matter *using your book or a dictionary.*

matter ______________________

New Vocabulary

Write a paragraph that uses all the vocabulary terms in a way that shows their meanings.

solid

gas

random motion

liquid

____

Academic Vocabulary

Use a dictionary to define distribute.

distribute ______________________

Name ______________________________ Date ____________

Main Idea | Details

What are states of matter?

I found this information on page ________.

Identify *the 4* states of matter, *and give an example of each.*

Four States of Matter	
State	Example
1.	
2.	
3.	
4.	

I found this information on page ________.

Model *the movement of particles in matter by* random motion. *Show particles as dots, and use arrows to show the direction of movement. Write a caption to explain your model.*

Caption: ______________________________

____

____

Summarize It

Summarize the main ideas of the above sections.

____

____

____

Name ______________________ Date __________

Main Idea — Details

Solids

I found this information on page ______.

Identify *the main* characteristics of solids.

____

____

____

Liquids

I found this information on page ______.

Compare *characteristics of* solids *and* liquids.

	Solids	Liquids
Shape	fixed	
Volume		fixed
Motion of particles		

Gases

I found this information on page ______.

Organize *information about* gases *in the outline.*

Characteristics of gases

1. Gas particles
   - **a.** ______________________
   - **b.** ______________________
2. Shape and volume of gases
   - **a.** ______________________
   - **b.** ______________________

SUMMARIZE IT

Summarize three main ideas from the above sections.

____

____

____

____

____

Name ______________________ Date __________

States of Matter

Lesson 2 Changes in States of Matter

Grade 8 Science Content Standards—5.d: Students know physical processes include freezing and boiling, in which a material changes form with no chemical reaction. Also covers 3.d, 3.e

Skim *Lesson 2 of your text. Write three questions that come to mind.*

1. ______________________
2. ______________________
3. ______________________

Review Vocabulary

Define potential energy *using your book or a dictionary.*

potential energy ______________________

New Vocabulary

Read the definitions below. Write the correct vocabulary term on the blank to the left of each definition.

______ temperature at which a liquid changes to a solid

______ measure of the average kinetic energy of all the particles in an object

______ change of a gas to a liquid

______ temperature at which a solid changes to a liquid

______ change of a liquid to a gas

______ change of a solid to a gas without first going through the liquid state

______ vaporization that occurs throughout a liquid

______ vaporization at the surface of a liquid

______ change of a gas to a solid without first going through the liquid state

______ temperature at which a liquid changes to a gas

Academic Vocabulary

Use a dictionary to define remove.

remove ______________________

Name ______________________________ Date ____________

Main Idea | **Details**

Temperature, Thermal Energy, and Heat

I found this information on page ________.

Summarize *how* kinetic energy *is related to* temperature.

____

____

____

I found this information on page ________.

Distinguish *two ways a material can change when its* thermal energy increases.

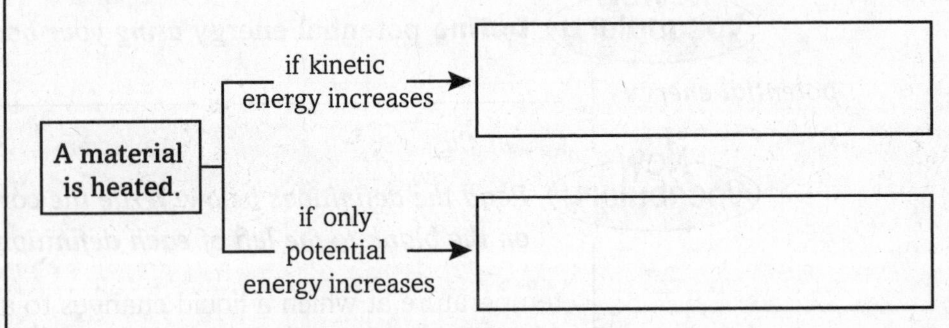

Changes Between the Solid and Liquid States

I found this information on page ________.

Compare melting *and* freezing *by labeling the diagram.*

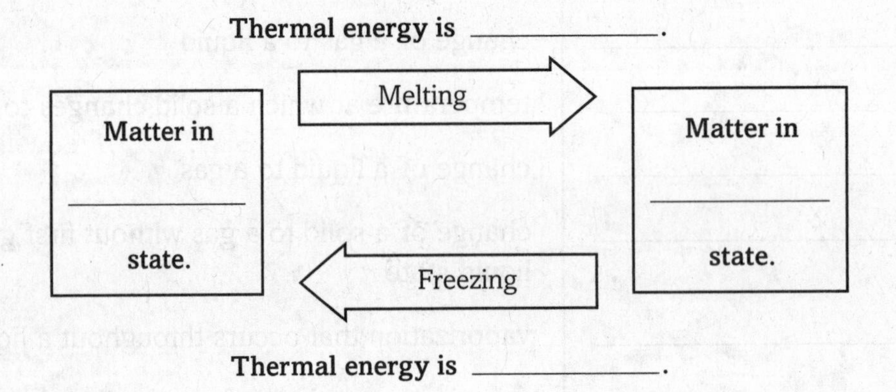

SUMMARIZE IT

Summarize the main ideas of the above sections.

____

____

____

____

____

Name _______________ Date _______________

Main Idea | **Details**

Changes Between Liquids and Gases

I found this information on page ______.

Compare and contrast vaporization, *and* condensation.

	What Happens	Location	Temperature
Vaporization: Boiling			
Vaporization: Evaporation			
Condensation			

Changing the State of Water

I found this information on page ______.

Label *the diagram below to show how a piece of ice changes as thermal energy is added to it. Use the terms provided.*

melting point boiling point solid gas liquid

increasing thermal energy

0°C 100°C

______ ______ ______

______ ______

Changes Between Solids and Gases

I found this information on page ______.

Contrast sublimation *and* deposition.

Sublimation: ______

Deposition: ______

SUMMARIZE IT Summarize the main ideas of the above sections.

______

______

______

______

______

Name ______________________ Date ______________

States of Matter Chapter Wrap-Up

Review the ideas you listed in the table at the beginning of the chapter. Cross out any incorrect information in the first column. Then complete the table by filling in the third column.

K What I know	W What I want to find out	L What I learned

Review

Use this checklist to help you study.

- ☐ Review the information you included in your Foldable.
- ☐ Study your *Science Notebook* on this chapter.
- ☐ Study the definitions of vocabulary words.
- ☐ Review daily homework assignments.
- ☐ Re-read the chapter and review the charts, graphs, and illustrations.
- ☐ Review the Standards Check at the end of each lesson.
- ☐ Look over the Standards Review at the end of the chapter.

SUMMARIZE IT After reading the chapter, write three sentences summarizing the main ideas of the chapter.

____

____

____

Name ______________________________ Date __________

The Periodic Table and Physical Properties

Grade 8 Science Content Standards—3.f: Students know how to use the periodic table to identify elements in simple compounds. Also covers: 5.d, 7.a, 7.b, 7.c

Before You Read

Before you read the chapter, think about what you know about the topic. List three things that you already know about the periodic table and physical properties in the first column. Then list three things that you would like to learn about the topic in the second column.

K What I know	W What I want to find out

Construct the Foldable as directed at the beginning of this chapter.

Science Journal

Write a paragraph explaining why you think it's helpful to keep your books, notebooks, and papers organized.

____

____

____

____

____

____

Name ________________________ Date ____________

The Periodic Table and Physical Properties

Lesson 1 Organization of the Periodic Table

Grade 8 Science Content Standards—3.f: Students know how to use the periodic table to identify elements in simple compounds. Also covers: 7.a

Scan *Lesson 1 of your book. Write two facts you discovered about the periodic table while scanning the lesson.*

1. ____________________

2. ____________________

Review Vocabulary

Define element. *Then use the term in a sentence.*

element ____________________

New Vocabulary

Use your book or a dictionary to define the following terms.

period ____________________

group ____________________

conductivity ____________________

halogen ____________________

Academic Vocabulary

Use your book or a dictionary to define the term conduct *as it is used in the following sentence.*

The chairperson of the committee will conduct the meeting.

conduct ____________________

Name ______________________ Date __________

Main Idea	Details
How are the elements arranged? *I found this information on page ______.*	**Organize** *the information found in an* element block *of the periodic table by filling in the graphic organizer.*

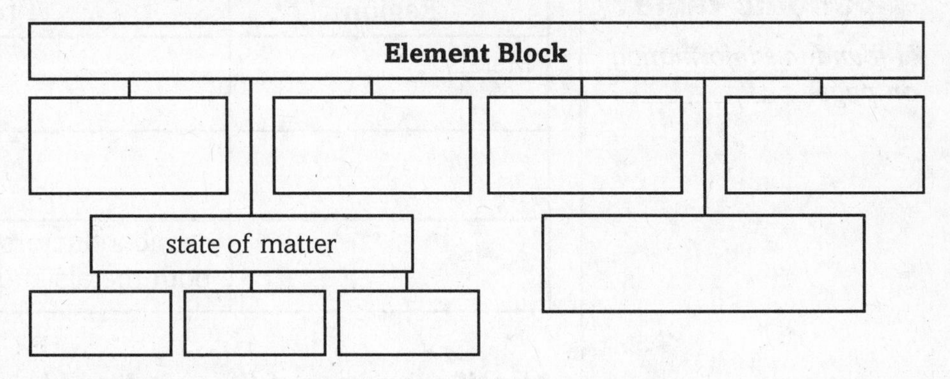

I found this information on page ______.	**Outline** *information about* periods *and* groups.

I. Periods

A. ______________________

B. ______________________

II. Groups

A. ______________________

B. Similar properties

1. Examples of chemical properties, Group 2

a. ______________________

b. ______________________

2. Examples of physical properties, Group 2

a. ______________________

b. ______________________

SUMMARIZE IT

Summarize two main ideas of the above sections.

____

____

____

Name ______________________________ Date ____________

Main Idea — **Details**

What are the regions of the periodic table?

I found this information on page ________.

Compare and contrast *the 3 regions of the periodic table.*

Region	Properties
Metals	
	semiconductors, properties of both metals and nonmetals

Identify *the areas of the periodic table in which* the most reactive metals and nonmetals *are found.*

____

____

I found this information on page ________.

Distinguish noble gases *from other nonmetals.*

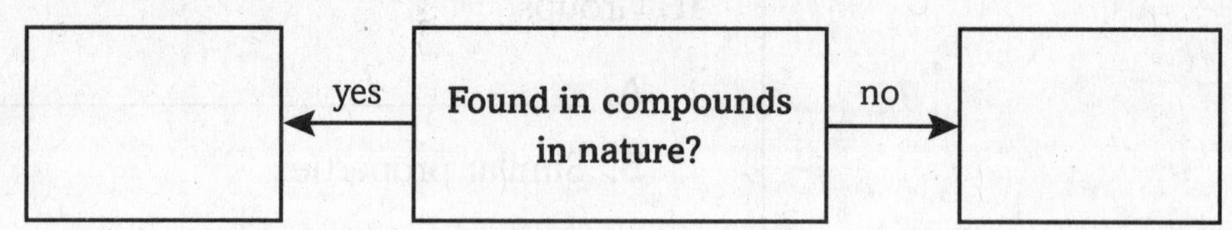

Are there other periodic tables?

I found this information on page ________.

Analyze *why different periodic tables are available to scientists.*

____

____

____

SUMMARIZE IT Summarize the main ideas of the above sections with two bullet points.

____

____

____

____

Name ______________________ Date __________

The Periodic Table and Physical Properties

Lesson 2 Isotopes and Radioactivity

Grade 8 Science Content Standards—7.b: Students know each element has a specific number of protons in the nucleus (the atomic number) and each isotope of the element has a different but specific number of neutrons in the nucleus. Also covers: 9.e

Scan *the lesson titles and bold words in Lesson 2. Write two facts that you discovered about the topic as you scanned the lesson.*

1. ______________________________

2. ______________________________

Review Vocabulary

Define isotope *using your book or a dictionary.*

isotopes ______________________________

New Vocabulary

Match the correct term with its definition.

__________ time it takes for a sample of a radioactive element to decay to half its original mass

__________ change of an unstable atomic nucleus into another nucleus as it emits particles and energy

__________ element that has only radioactive isotopes

__________ radioactive element made by scientists or during nuclear reactions

__________ describes a nucleus that is unstable and undergoes radioactive decay

__________ machine capable of making particles move very quickly

__________ process in which an atom of one element is changed into an atom of another element

Academic Vocabulary

Use your book or a dictionary to find the scientific definition of the term stable.

stable ______________________________

Main Idea | **Details**

Isotopes - Different Numbers of Neutrons

I found this information on page ______.

Contrast *three* isotopes of carbon. *Complete the table.*

	Mass Number	Atomic Number	Number of Protons	Number of Neutrons
Carbon-12				
Carbon-13				
Carbon-14				

I found this information on page ______.

Analyze *why isotopes have similar chemical properties.*

____

____

What is radioactive decay?

I found this information on page ______.

Compare and contrast *two types of* radioactive decay. *Complete the diagrams to show what happens when an atom releases an* alpha particle *and a* beta particle.

An atom releases an alpha particle. → The atom loses ______ and ______. → The element becomes ______ ______ ______ ______.

An atom releases a beta particle. → The atom loses ______ ______ and gains ______. → The element becomes ______ ______ ______.

SUMMARIZE IT Write two sentences to summarize the above section.

____

____

____

Name ______________________ Date ____________

Main Idea | **Details**

What is radioactive decay?

I found this information on page ________.

Identify *two* uses of radioactivity.

1. ______________________

2. ______________________

I found this information on page ________.

Summarize *how uranium's long* half-life *explains why it is still found in nature.*

____

____

____

How are elements discovered and named?

I found this information on page ________.

Sequence *the steps used by scientists to produce* synthetic elements. *Complete the flow chart.*

Scientists bombard an atom with ______________________ ______________________.

Particles might ______________________ ______________________.

I found this information on page ________.

Create *a concept map about the rules used by scientists to decide whether a new synthetic element has been created.*

Rules for New Elements

SUMMARIZE IT Summarize the main ideas of the above sections.

____

____

____

Name ______________________ Date __________

The Periodic Table and Physical Properties

Lesson 3 Physical Properties and Changes

Grade 8 Science Content Standards—5.d: Students know physical properties include freezing and boiling, in which a material changes form with no chemical reaction. Also covers: 7.c, 9.a

Skim *Lesson 3. Write two questions that come to mind. Look for the answers as you read.*

1. ______________________

2. ______________________

Review Vocabulary

Define density *using its scientific meaning.*

density ______________________

New Vocabulary

Use your book or a dictionary to define the following terms.

physical property ______________________

melting point ______________________

boiling point ______________________

thermal conductivity ______________________

physical change ______________________

Academic Vocabulary

Use your book or a dictionary to define transfer.

transfer ______________________

Name ______________________________ Date ____________

Main Idea | **Details**

What is a physical property?

I found this information on page ________.

Create *a graphic organizer to identify the 10* physical properties.

I found this information on page ________.

Draw *and label an arrow to show how the* melting point *and* boiling point *of a substance depend on* the attraction between particles.

less attraction → more attraction

I found this information on page ________.

Complete *the following paragraph to summarize information about density and hardness.*

Density is the ______________________ of a substance. The density of a substance is ____________ if its particles are packed tightly together. Hardness shows ______________________ ______________________.

SUMMARIZE IT Summarize three main ideas from the above section.

____

____

____

____

Name ______________________ Date ____________

Main Idea | **Details**

What is a physical property?

I found this information on page ______.

Outline information *about* thermal *and* electrical conductivity.

I. Thermal conductivity
   A. Ability to transfer heat through ______
   B. ______
      1. ______
      2. ______
   C. Low conductivity in gases
      1. ______
      2. ______
II. Electrical conductivity
   A. Ability to transfer ______
   B. ______
   C. Plastic has ______.

What is a physical change?

I found this information on page ______.

Organize *information about* examples of physical changes.

Physical Change	Description	Example
Dissolving		
		mixing iron filings and sand
	changing a substance from its original state to a solid, liquid, or gas	

SUMMARIZE IT **Highlight one main idea of this section in the paragraph below.**

Ice cream melts into a liquid. Bubble gum is blown into a sphere. A piece of modeling clay is shaped into a statue. These are physical changes. A physical change is any change in size, shape, or state of matter in which the identity of the substance remains unchanged.

Name ______________________ Date ____________

Tie It Together

The Periodic Table

Create a periodic table puzzle.

1. Obtain six pieces of paper. Cut each piece of paper into six equal pieces.
2. Make an element box for each of the first 36 elements in the periodic table. On each element box, fill in only part of the information shown on the periodic table. You might write the atomic mass, the atomic number, or the symbol.
3. Swap sets of partially completed element boxes with a partner.
4. Complete each element box in your partner's set.
5. Then, piece together your partner's periodic table in order.

Name ______________________________ Date __________

The Periodic Table and Physical Properties Chapter Wrap-Up

Review the ideas you listed in the table at the beginning of the chapter. Cross out any incorrect information in the first column. Then complete the table by filling in the third .

K What I know	W What I want to find out	L What I learned

Review

Use this checklist to help you study.

- ☐ Review the information you included in your Foldable.
- ☐ Study your *Science Notebook* on this chapter.
- ☐ Study the definitions of vocabulary words.
- ☐ Review daily homework assignments.
- ☐ Re-read the chapter and review the charts, graphs, and illustrations.
- ☐ Review the Standards Check at the end of each lesson.
- ☐ Look over the Standards Review at the end of the chapter.

SUMMARIZE IT **After reading this chapter, write one or two summary sentences for each lesson to illustrate the chapter's main ideas.**

____

____

____

____

____

Name ______________________ Date ________

Chemical Reactions

Grade 8 Science Content Standards—3.b: Students know that compounds are formed by combining two or more different elements and that compounds have properties different from their constituent elements. Also covers: 3.f, 5.a, 5.b, 5.c, 7.c

Before You Read

Before you read the chapter, think about what you know about the topic. List three things that you already know about the chemical reactions in the first column. Then list three things that you would like to learn about chemical reactions in the second column.

K What I know	W What I want to find out

FOLDABLES™ Study Organizer *Construct the Foldable as directed at the beginning of this chapter.*

Science Journal

Write three questions you would like to ask a chemist about air bags.

Name ______________________________ Date ____________

Chemical Reactions

Lesson 1 Chemical Properties and Changes

Grade 8 Science Content Standards—7.c: Students know substances can be classified by their properties, including their melting temperature, density, hardness, and thermal and electrical conductivity. Also covers: 5.a

Scan *the headings in Lesson 1 of your book. Identify three topics that will be discussed.*

1. ______________________________
2. ______________________________
3. ______________________________

Review Vocabulary

Define physical property, *using your book or a dictionary. Then use the term in a scientific sentence.*

physical property ______________________________

____

New Vocabulary

Write a paragraph using all of the vocabulary terms.

chemical property
chemical change
dissolving

____

Academic Vocabulary

Use a dictionary to define compound.

compound ______________________________

Name ______________________ Date ________

Lesson 1 Chemical Properties and Changes (continued)

Main Idea | Details

Ability to Change

I found this information on page ______.

Compare and contrast chemical properties *and* physical properties *by filling in the Venn diagram using the phrases listed.*

- used to identify a substance
- observed without changing the identity of a substance
- ability to burn is an example
- color is an example
- observed by changing the identity of a substance

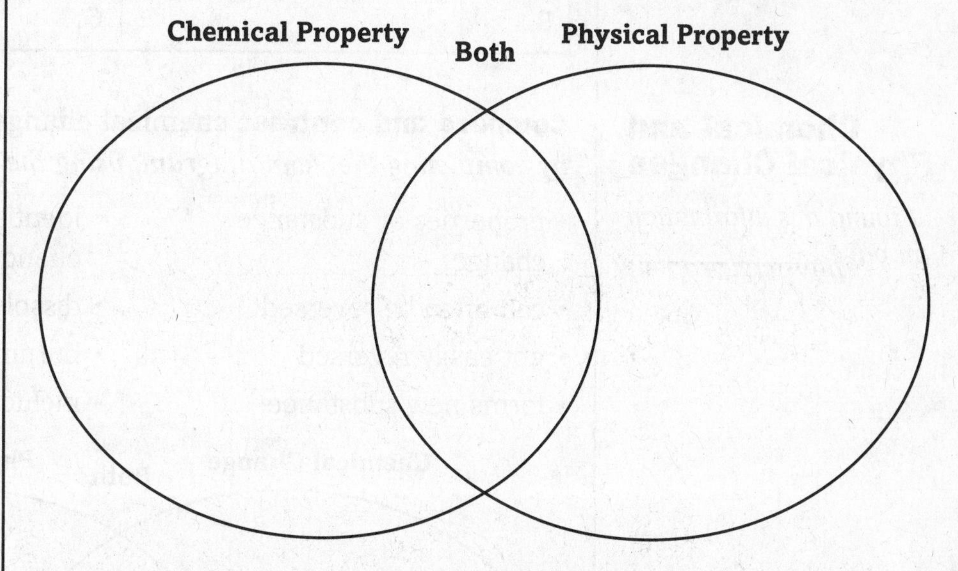

I found this information on page ______.

Identify *at least one chemical property for each substance.*

Substance	Chemical Property
Iron	
Paper	
Helium gas	
Hydrogen gas	
Copper	

SUMMARIZE IT Summarize the main ideas of the above section.

____

____

____

Name ______________________ Date ____________

Main Idea — Details

Ability to Change

I found this information on page ______.

Identify *six examples of* physical properties of matter.

Examples of Physical Properties of Matter	
1.	4.
2.	5.
3.	6.

Chemical and Physical Changes

I found this information on page ______.

Compare and contrast chemical changes *and* physical changes *by completing the Venn diagram, using the phrases listed.*

- properties of substance change
- can often be reversed
- not easily reversed
- forms new substance
- identity of substance does not change
- dissolving is an example
- burning is an example
- includes changes of state

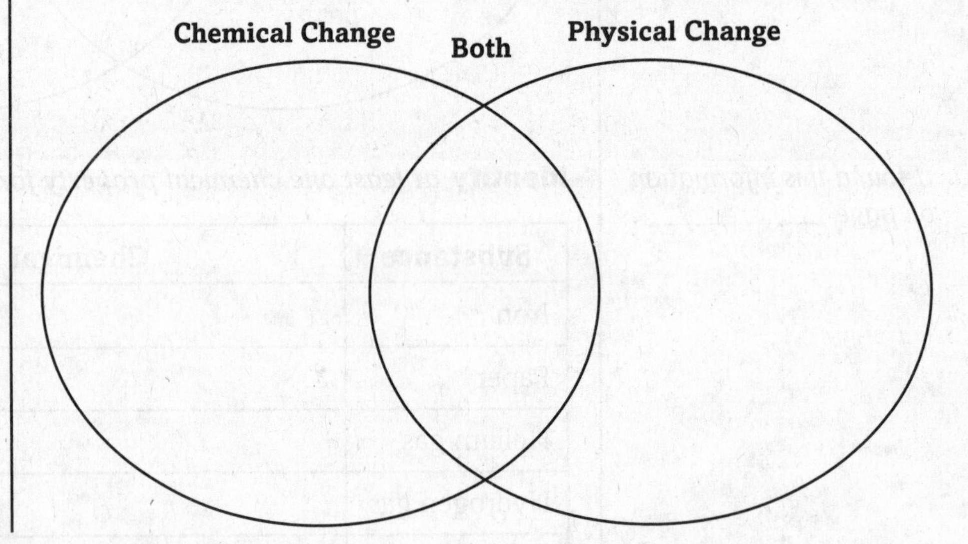

SUMMARIZE IT Summarize three main ideas of the above sections.

____

____

____

____

Name ____________________ Date __________

Chemical Reactions

Lesson 2 Chemical Equations

Grade 8 Science Content Standards—3.b: Students know that compounds are formed by combining two or more different elements and that compounds have properties different from their constituent elements. Also covers: 3.f, 5.b

Skim *Lesson 2 of your book. Write three questions that come to mind. Look for answers to your questions as you read the lesson.*

1. ____________________
2. ____________________
3. ____________________

Review Vocabulary **Define** molecule, *using your book or a dictionary.*

molecule ____________________

New Vocabulary *Read the definitions below. Write the correct vocabulary term on the blank to the left of each definition.*

__________ new substance formed in a chemical reaction

__________ scientific principle stating that the total mass before a chemical reaction is the same as the total mass after the reaction

__________ molecule that contains two atoms

__________ starting substance in a chemical reaction

__________ number in front of a symbol or formula that tells how many molecules or formula units take part in a reaction

Academic Vocabulary *Use a dictionary to define* precise. *Then use the term in a sentence to show how it is used in science.*

precise ____________________

Name ______________________________ Date ____________

Main Idea	Details
Is matter conserved in chemical reactions? *I found this information on page ______.*	**Rephrase** *the* law of conservation of mass *in your own words.* ______________________________ ______________________________ ______________________________
How do you write a chemical equation? *I found this information on page ______.*	**Label** *the* reactants *and* product *in the equation below.* tin + oxygen gas → tin oxide **Summarize** *two limitations of word equations.* ______________________________ ______________________________
I found this information on page ______.	**Distinguish** *between an* element, *a* diatomic molecule, *and a* compound. *Give an example of each, including the symbol.*

	What is it?	Example	Symbol
Element			
Diatomic molecule			
Compound			

SUMMARIZE IT

Summarize the main ideas of the above sections of this lesson.

____

____

____

____

Name ______________________ Date ____________

Main Idea | **Details**

How do you balance a chemical equation?

I found this information on page ______.

Analyze *when a chemical equation is balanced.*

____

____

Contrast *the use of* subscripts *and* coefficients *in chemical equations.*

Subscript	Coefficient
Tells	Tells

Equations for Common Chemical Reactions

I found this information on page ______.

Sequence *the steps involved in balancing an equation. Complete the flow chart.*

Write the ______________________.

↓

Count ______________________.

↓

Place coefficients ______________________

______________________.

Complete *each equation below to summarize its chemical reaction.*

Reaction of methane:

$\_\_\_\_ + \_\_\_\_ O_2 \rightarrow CO_2 + \_\_\_\_ H_2O$

Baking soda and vinegar:

$\_\_\_\_ + \_\_\_\_ \rightarrow \_\_\_\_ + \_\_\_\_ + NaC_2H_3O_2$

SUMMARIZE IT Summarize two main ideas from the above sections.

____

____

Name ______________________ Date ______

Chemical Reactions

Lesson 3 Energy and Chemical Change

Grade 8 Science Content Standards—5.c: Students know chemical reactions usually liberate heat or absorb heat.

Scan *Lesson 3 of your book. Look at the headings, bold words, and pictures. Write three facts that you learn about energy and chemical change.*

1. ______________________

2. ______________________

3. ______________________

Review Vocabulary

Use chemical bond *in a sentence to show its scientific meaning.*

chemical bond ______________________

New Vocabulary

Define *each vocabulary term, using your book or a dictionary.*

law of conservation of energy ______________________

exothermic process ______________________

endothermic process ______________________

Academic Vocabulary

Use a dictionary to define function. *Then write a sentence to show its scientific meaning.*

function ______________________

Main Idea | **Details**

Energy and Chemical Reactions

I found this information on page ______.

Identify *five forms of energy that are released or used in chemical reactions.*

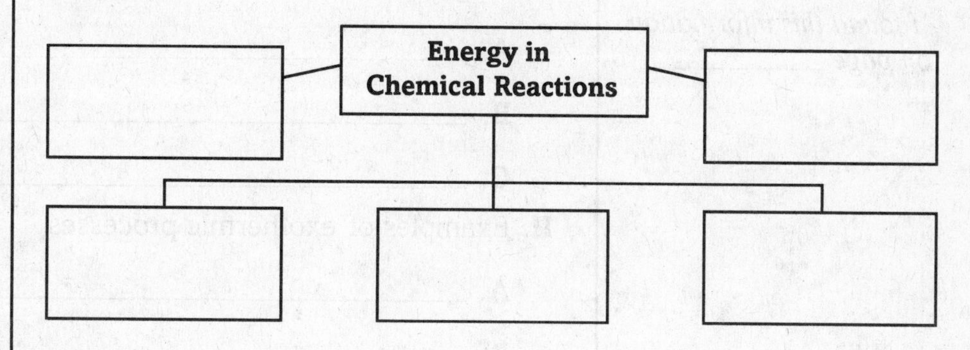

I found this information on page ______.

Rephrase *the* law of conservation of energy *in your own words.*

____

____

____

Net Release of Energy

I found this information on page ______.

Organize *information about* exothermic processes. *Complete the concept map.*

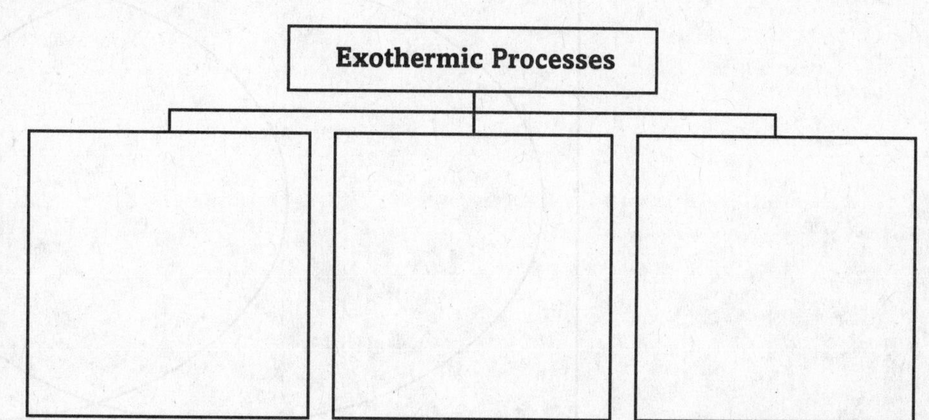

SUMMARIZE IT Summarize the main ideas of the above sections of this lesson.

____

____

____

____

Name ______________________ Date ____________

Main Idea — Details

Net Absorption of Energy

I found this information on page ______.

Outline *information about* endothermic processes.

I. Properties of endothermic processes

A. ______

B. ______

C. ______

II. Examples of exothermic processes

A. ______

B. ______

I found this information on page ______.

Compare and contrast *endothermic and exothermic processes by completing the Venn diagram with the terms below.*

- net absorption of energy
- net release of energy
- may involve heat
- occurs as bonds break and reform

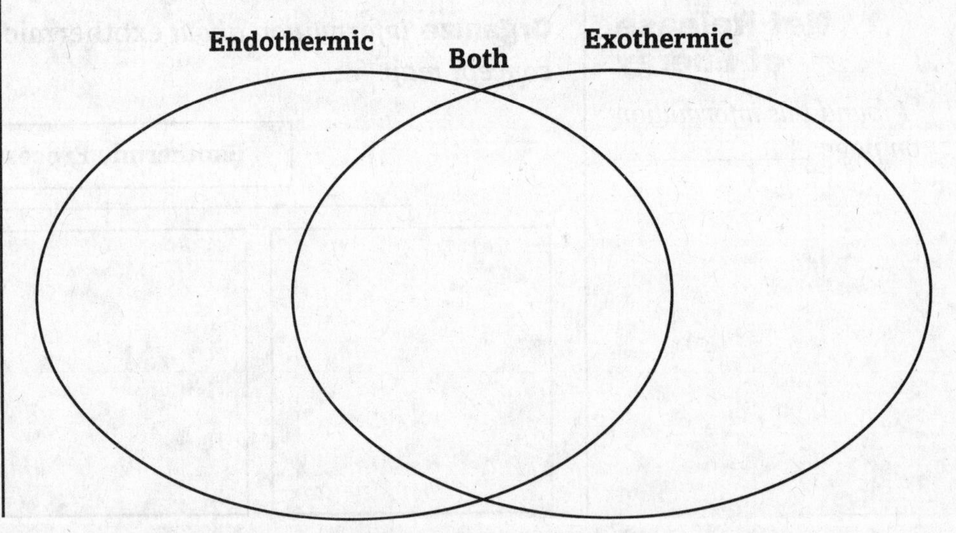

SUMMARIZE IT

Summarize the main ideas of this section in two bullet points.

______

______

______

______

Name ______________________________ Date ____________

Tie It Together

Chemical Reactions

Use the information in the paragraph below and what you learned in the chapter to balance the chemical equation given and answer the questions.

Photosynthesis is the process by which plants make food in the form of the sugar glucose ($C_6H_{12}O_6$). Plants make glucose by using light energy to combine carbon dioxide (CO_2) and water (H_2O). In addition to glucose, oxygen (O_2) is also formed. The chemical equation for photosynthesis is shown.

Chemical Equation for Photosynthesis: $CO_2 + H_2O + \text{Light Energy} \rightarrow C_6H_{12}O_6 + O_2$

Count the atoms in the reactants and products.

Reactants: __________ + __________

Number of carbon atoms: __________

Number of hydrogen atoms: __________

Number of oxygen atoms: __________

Products: __________ + __________

Number of carbon atoms: __________

Number of hydrogen atoms: __________

Number of oxygen atoms: __________

Balanced Equation: $6CO_2 + 6H_2O + \text{energy} \rightarrow C_6H_{12}O_6 + 6O_2$

Count the atoms on each side of the balanced equation.

Reactants:

Number of carbon atoms: __________

Number of hydrogen atoms: __________

Number of oxygen atoms: __________

Products:

Number of carbon atoms: __________

Number of hydrogen atoms: __________

Number of oxygen atoms: __________

Analysis

1. Summarize photosynthesis in a word equation.

____

____

2. Classify photosynthesis as an endothermic or an exothermic reaction. Support your response with a specific example.

____

____

____

Name ______________________ Date ____________

Chemical Reactions Chapter Wrap-Up

Review the ideas you listed in the table at the beginning of the chapter. Cross out any incorrect information in the first column. Then complete the table by filling in the third column.

K What I know	W What I want to find out	L What I learned

Review

Use this checklist to help you study.

- ☐ Review the information you included in your Foldable.
- ☐ Study your *Science Notebook* on this chapter.
- ☐ Study the definitions of vocabulary words.
- ☐ Review daily homework assignments.
- ☐ Re-read the chapter and review the charts, graphs, and illustrations.
- ☐ Review the Standards Check at the end of each lesson.
- ☐ Look over the Standards Review at the end of the chapter.

SUMMARIZE IT **After reading the chapter, write a sentence or two summarizing the main idea of each lesson.**

____

____

____

____

Name ______________________________ Date ____________

Acids and Bases in Solution

Grade 8 Science Content Standards—5.e: Students know how to determine whether a solution is acidic, basic, or neutral. Also covers: 7.c

Before You Read

Before you read the chapter, respond to these statements.

1. Write an **A** if you agree with the statement.
2. Write a **D** if you disagree with the statement.

Before You Read	Acids and Bases in Solution
	• A compound is a type of mixture.
	• You can dissolve any amount of salt in a glass of water.
	• Soap is acidic.
	• A substance that is neutral is neither an acid nor a base.

Construct the Foldable as directed at the beginning of this chapter.

Science Journal

Write a brief paragraph on what you think these rocks are made from.

____

____

____

____

____

____

____

Name ______________________ Date ______________

Acids and Bases in Solution

Lesson 1 Solutions

Grade 8 Science Content Standards—7.c: Students know substances can be classified by their properties, including their melting temperature, density, hardness, and thermal and electrical conductivity.

Scan *the* What You'll Learn *statements for Lesson 1 of your book. Identify two topics that will be discussed.*

1. Acids in solutions

2. Bases in solutions

Define liquid *using your book or a dictionary.*

liquid Matter with ______________________

Read the definitions below. Write the correct vocabulary term on the blank to the left of each definition.

______________	homogeneous mixture
______________	matter that has the same composition and properties throughout
______________	mixture in which the substances are not evenly mixed
______________	substance that dissolves in a solution
______________	two or more substances that are evenly mixed on the atomic level but are not bonded together
______________	substance used to dissolve a solute
______________	combination of two or more substances that can be separated by physical means

Academic Vocabulary

Use a dictionary to define individual.

individual ______________________

Name ______________________ Date ____________

Main Idea — Details

What are acids and bases?

I found this information on page ______.

Identify *at least two examples of everyday* acids *and* bases.

Acids	Bases

Acids

I found this information on page ______.

Summarize *important facts about* acids. *List one fact on each line.*

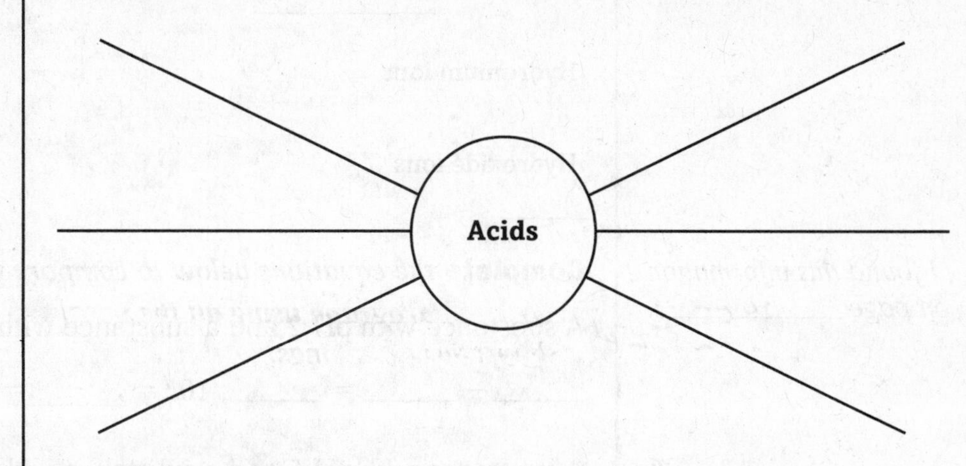

Bases

I found this information on page ______.

Organize *information about* bases. *Complete the diagram.*

Definition:	Common Properties:
Examples:	Common Uses:

(Center: Bases)

SUMMARIZE IT

Summarize the main ideas of the above sections with two bullet points.

____

____

Name ______________________ Date __________

Main Idea	Details
What is pH?	**Label** *the locations of* acids, bases, *and* neutral substances *on the pH scale below. Draw arrows to show how the concentrations of* hydronium ions *and* hydroxide ions *change across the pH scale.*
I found this information on page ________.	

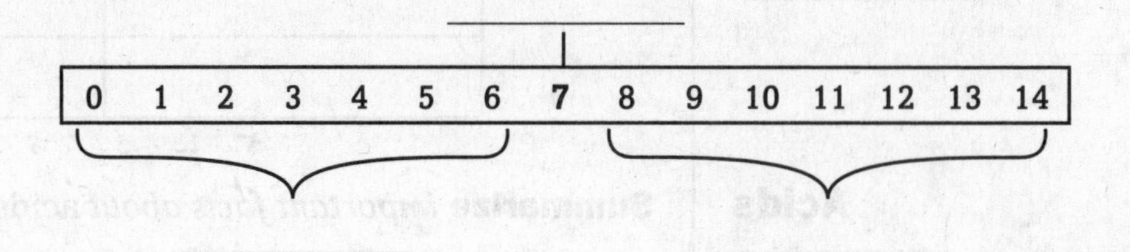

Hydronium ions

Hydroxide ions

I found this information on page ________.

Complete *the equations below to compare* pH values.

A substance with pH 2 and a substance with pH 1

______ − ______ = ______; 10^n = ______ = ______ times more acidic

A substance with pH 5 and a substance with pH 2

______ − ______ = ______; 10^n = ______ = ______ times more acidic

I found this information on page ________.

Define neutralization.

____

____

SUMMARIZE IT

Summarize three main ideas of the above sections using bullet points.

____

____

____

____

____

Main Idea | **Details**

What is pH?

I found this information on page ______________.

Label *the neutralization reaction below to identify its reactants and products as an acid, a salt, a base, and water.*

$2HCl + Mg(OH)_2$ → $MgCl_2 + 2H_20$

______________ + ______________ ______________ + ______________

How is pH measured?

I found this information on page ______________.

Compare and contrast *the methods for measuring pH. Complete the Venn diagram with the facts below. Then describe what a* pH meter *is.*

- change color
- universal indicator is an example
- litmus paper is an example
- approximate pH

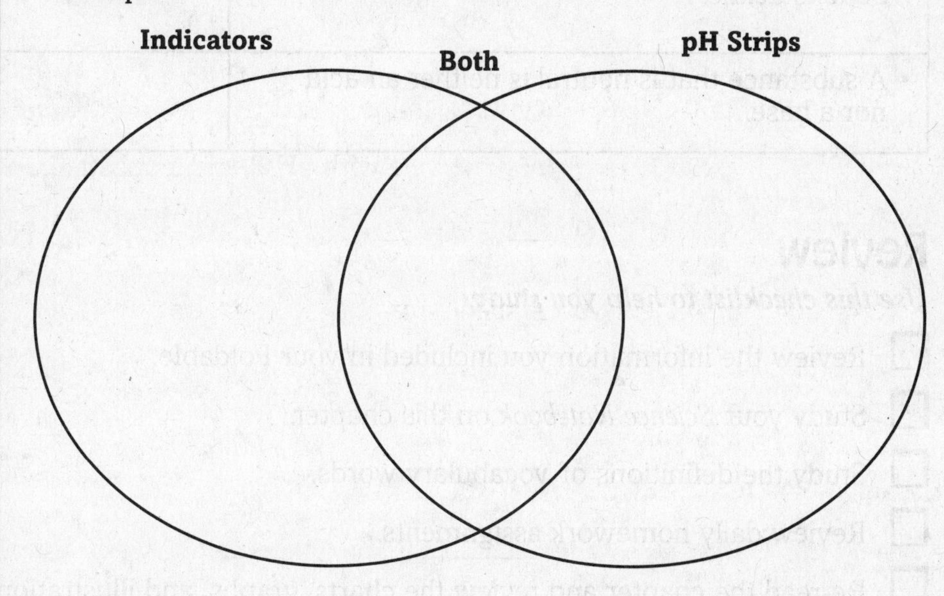

A pH meter is an ______________ with an ______________ that is sensitive to the ______________ in a solution.

SUMMARIZE IT Summarize three main ideas of the above sections.

____

____

____

Name ______________________________ Date __________

Acids and Bases in Solution

Chapter Wrap-Up

Now that you have read the chapter, think about what you have learned and complete the table below. Compare your previous answers to these.

1. Write an **A** if you agree with the statement.
2. Write a **D** if you disagree with the statement.

Acids and Bases in Solution	After You Read
• A compound is a type of mixture.	
• You can dissolve any amount of salt in a glass of water.	
• Soap is acidic.	
• A substance that is neutral is neither an acid nor a base.	

Review

Use this checklist to help you study.

- ☐ Review the information you included in your Foldable.
- ☐ Study your *Science Notebook* on this chapter.
- ☐ Study the definitions of vocabulary words.
- ☐ Review daily homework assignments.
- ☐ Re-read the chapter and review the charts, graphs, and illustrations.
- ☐ Review the Standards Check at the end of each lesson.
- ☐ Look over the Standards Review at the end of the chapter.

SUMMARIZE IT

After studying the chapter, write one summary sentence for each lesson to illustrate the chapter's main ideas.

____

____

____

Name ______________________ Date ______________

Chemistry of Living Systems

Grade 8 Science Content Standards—6.b: Students know that living organisms are made of molecules consisting largely of carbon, hydrogen, oxygen, phosphorus, and sulfur. Also covers: 3.c, 6.a, 6.c

Before You Read

Before you read the chapter, think about what you know about the topic. List three things that you already know about the chemistry of living systems in the first column. Then list three things that you would like to learn about the chemistry of living systems in the second column.

K What I know	W What I want to find out

Construct the Foldable as directed at the beginning of this chapter.

Science Journal

What molecules do you think bears and humans have in common?

Name ______________________ Date __________

Chemistry of Living Systems

Lesson 1 Chemistry of Life

Grade 8 Science Content Standards—6.b: Students know that living organisms are made of molecules consisting largely of carbon, hydrogen, nitrogen, oxygen, phosphorus, and sulfur. Also covers: 6.a, 6.c

Scan *Lesson 1 of your book. Read the headings and bold words and look at the pictures. Write three things that you discovered about the chemistry of living systems.*

1. ______________________
2. ______________________
3. ______________________

Review Vocabulary

Define element *as it is used in science. Use your book or a dictionary to help.*

element ______________________

New Vocabulary

Use your book or a dictionary to define the vocabulary terms.

biomass ______________________

polar molecule ______________________

nonpolar molecule ______________________

Academic Vocabulary

Use your book or a dictionary to define cycle. *Then use it in a sentence to show its scientific meaning.*

cycle ______________________

Name ______________________________ Date __________

Main Idea | **Details**

Elements of Life

I found this information on page ________.

Identify *the 6 elements that make up most of Earth's* biomass.

1. ______________ 4. ______________
2. ______________ 5. ______________
3. ______________ 6. ______________

Cycles in Life

I found this information on page ________.

Create *a cycle map in the space below showing the movement of carbon in the* carbon cycle. *Include labels to identify the form of carbon at each stage of the cycle. Use arrows to link the processes.*

I found this information on page ________.

Model *the path of* nitrogen *as it cycles through the environment. Complete the flow chart.*

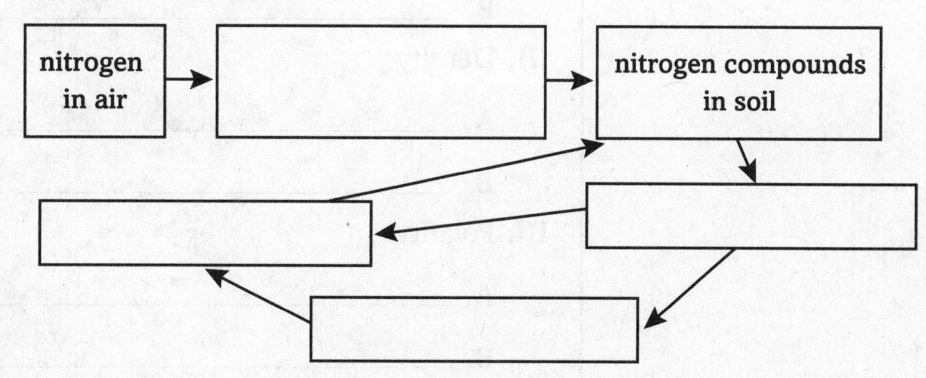

SUMMARIZE IT Summarize the main ideas of the above sections.

Main Idea | **Details**

Cycles of Matter

I found this information on page ______.

Summarize *how* phosphorus cycles *through the environment.*

______

______

______

Water and Living Organisms

I found this information on page ______.

Analyze *the* importance of water to organisms. *Complete the table.*

Organisms	How Water is Used
Animals	
Plants	
One-celled organisms	

I found this information on page ______.

Outline *information about* the unique characteristics of water.

I. Resistance to temperature change

A. ______

B. ______

II. Density

A. ______

B. ______

III. Polarity

A. ______

B. ______

C. ______

SUMMARIZE IT Summarize two main ideas of the above sections.

______

______

Name ______________________________ Date ______________

Chemistry of Living Systems

Lesson 2 Carbon Compounds

Grade 8 Science Content Standardss—6.a: Students know that carbon, because of its ability to combine in many ways with itself and other elements, has a central role in the chemistry of living organisms. Also covers: 3.c, 6.b, 6.c

Skim *Lesson 2 of your book. Write three questions that come to mind. Look for answers to your questions as you read the lesson.*

1. ______________________________
2. ______________________________
3. ______________________________

Review Vocabulary

Define covalent bond *using your book or a dictionary.*

covalent bond ______________________________

New Vocabulary

Write the correct vocabulary term on the blank to the left of each definition.

______________ molecule that contains only carbon and hydrogen atoms

______________ compound that contains at least one double or triple bond between carbon atoms

______________ group of atoms that replaces a hydrogen atom in an organic compound

______________ compound that contains the element carbon

______________ organic compound that is a basic building block of proteins

______________ compound that contains only single bonds between carbon atoms

Academic Vocabulary

Use your book or a dictionary to define the scientific meaning of **substitute.**

substitute ______________________________

Name ______________________ Date __________

Main Idea | **Details**

Organic Compounds

I found this information on page ______.

Identify the element found in all organic compounds.

____

I found this information on page ______.

Compare and contrast ethylene *and* ethyne *by using the phrases listed to fill in the graphic organizer.*

- plant hormone
- organic compound
- used for welding
- double bond between carbon atoms
- triple bond between carbon atoms
- made up only of carbon and hydrogen

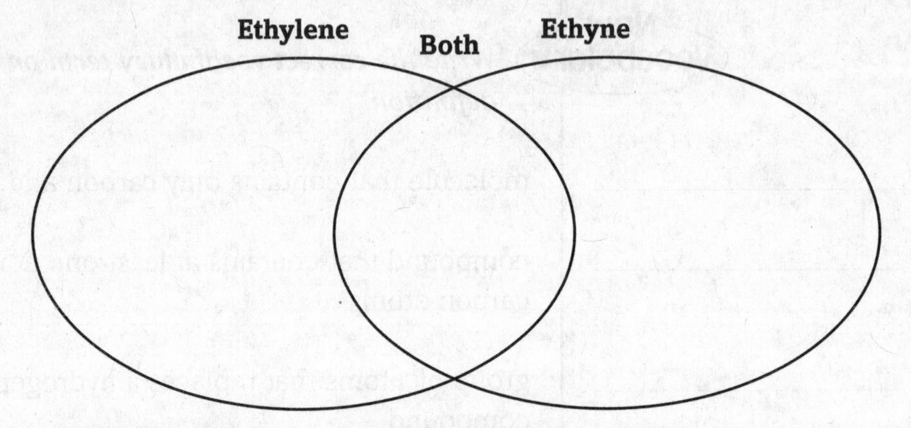

I found this information on page ______.

Classify *the 2 groups of* hydrocarbon compounds.

	Saturated	Unsaturated
Bonds between carbon atoms		
Examples		

SUMMARIZE IT Summarize two main ideas of the above section.

____

____

____

Name ______________________________ Date ____________

Main Idea | **Details**

Organic Compounds

I found this information on page ________.

Model *the first four* hydrocarbons. *Draw each compound and write its chemical formula.*

Methane	Ethane	Propane	Butane
Formula:	Formula:	Formula:	Formula:

Complete *the table to summarize what information each part of a hydrocarbon's name provides.*

Prefix	Root	Suffix

Analyze *the hydrocarbons below.* *Identify* how many carbon atoms *are in each hydrocarbon and* what type of bonds *the carbon forms.*

Name: Hexene

Carbon atoms: ________

Type of bonds: ________

Name: Butyne

Carbon atoms: ________

Type of bonds: ________

SUMMARIZE IT Rephrase two main ideas of the above section.

____

____

____

____

Name ______________________ Date __________

Main Idea | **Details**

Substituted Hydrocarbons

I found this information on page ______.

Organize *information about* alcohols. *Complete the concept map.*

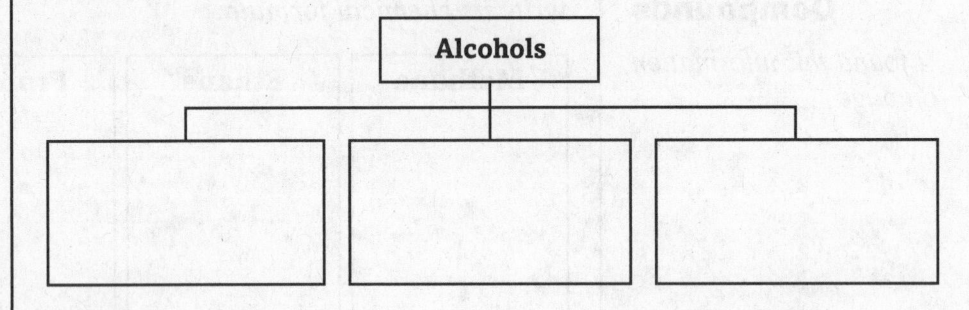

Summarize *the functional group found in* carboxylic acids.

____

____

Contrast *the functional groups found in* amines *and* amino acids.

	Amines	Amino Acids
Functional group(s)		

Shapes of Molecules

I found this information on page ______.

Create *drawings to show* linear, planar, *and* tetrahedral *molecules.*

Linear	Planar	Tetrahedral

SUMMARIZE IT Summarize the main ideas of the above sections.

____

____

____

Name ______________________ **Date** ____________

Chemistry of Living Systems

Lesson 3 Compounds of Life

Grade 8 Science Content Standards—6.c: Students know that living organisms have many different kinds of molecules, including small ones, such as water and salt, and very large ones, such as carbohydrates, fats, proteins, and DNA. Also covers: 6.a, 6.b

Scan *the headings of Lesson 3 of your book. Predict three topics that will be discussed.*

1. ______________________
2. ______________________
3. ______________________

Review Vocabulary

Define compound *using your book or a dictionary.*

compound ______________________

New Vocabulary

Use your book or a dictionary to define the following terms.

lipid ______________________

biomolecule ______________________

nucleic acid ______________________

carbohydrate ______________________

synthetic polymer ______________________

monomer ______________________

Academic Vocabulary

Define random *using a dictionary. Then use the term in a sentence to show its scientific meaning.*

random ______________________

Name ______________________ Date ____________

Main Idea | **Details**

Polymers

I found this information on page ______.

Complete *the statement to describe* polymers.

Polymers are made up of ______ and can be ______ or ______.

Biological Molecules

I found this information on page ______.

Identify *the* biomolecules *formed by the joining of each type of monomer.*

Amino acids: ______________________

Sugars: ______________________

Nucleotides: ______________________

Summarize the chemical composition of a lipid.

____

____

I found this information on page ______.

Analyze *the structure of* DNA *and* RNA. *Complete the diagram.*

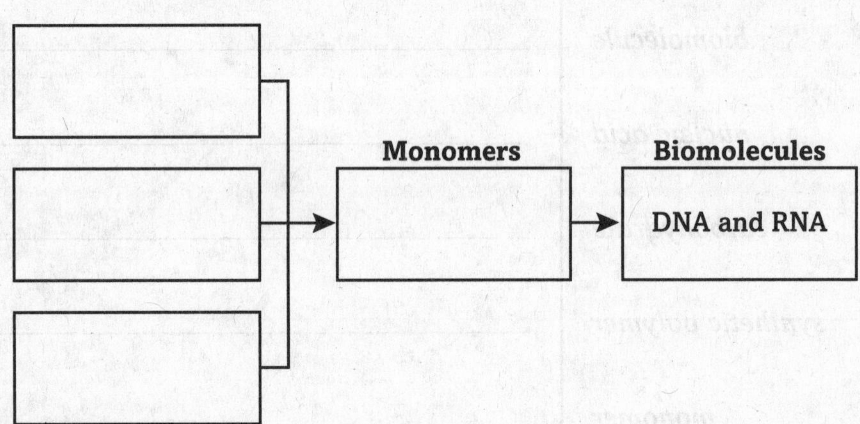

SUMMARIZE IT Summarize three main ideas from the above sections.

____

____

____

____

Name ______________________ Date __________

Main Idea	Details
Biological Molecules *I found this information on page* ______.	**Contrast** *the 2 main* types of fats. Saturated fats have ______ bonds between carbon atoms and are ______ at room temperature. Unsaturated fats have ______ ______ and are ______ at room temperature. **Create** *a concept map about* complex carbohydrates. *Include at least three facts.*
Other Elements in the Human Body *I found this information on page* ______.	**Identify** the function of each element in the human body. 1. Fluorine ______ 2. Iron ______ 3. Magnesium ______ 4. Calcium ______ 5. Copper ______ 6. Sulfur ______

SUMMARIZE IT Summarize the main ideas of the above sections.

______

______

______

Name ______________________________ Date ____________

Chemistry of Living Systems

Chapter Wrap-Up

Review the ideas you listed in the table at the beginning of the chapter. Cross out any incorrect information in the first column. Then complete the table by filling in the third column.

K What I know	W What I want to find out	L What I learned

Review

Use this checklist to help you study.

- ☐ Review the information you included in your Foldable.
- ☐ Study your *Science Notebook* on this chapter.
- ☐ Study the definitions of vocabulary words.
- ☐ Review daily homework assignments.
- ☐ Re-read the chapter and review the charts, graphs, and illustrations.
- ☐ Review the Standards Check at the end of each lesson.
- ☐ Look over the Standards Review at the end of the chapter.

SUMMARIZE IT **After studying the chapter, write one summary sentence for each lesson to illustrate the chapter's main ideas.**

____

____

____

____

Name _______________ Date _______________

Our Solar System

Grade 8 Science Content Standards—4.e: Students know the appearance, general composition, relative position and size, and motion of objects in the solar system, including planets, planetary satellites, comets, and asteroids. Also covers: 2.g, 4.c, 4.d

Before You Read

Before you read the chapter, think about what you know about the topic. List three things that you already know about the solar system in the first column. Then list three things that you would like to learn about the solar system in the second column.

K What I know	W What I want to find out

Construct the Foldable as directed at the beginning of this chapter.

Science Journal

How do you define a planet? Make a list of several criteria you would use to decide which objects would be classifed as planets.

Name ______________________________ Date ____________

Our Solar System

Lesson 1 Structure of the Solar System

Grade 8 Science Content Standards—4.e: Students know the appearance, general composition, relative position and size, and motion of objects in the solar system, including planets, planetary satellites, comets, and asteroids.
Also covers: 2.g, 4.c, 4.d

Skim *Lesson 1. Pay attention to the section headings and bold words. Write 3 topics you predict will be covered in this lesson.*

1. ______________________________
2. ______________________________
3. ______________________________

Review Vocabulary

Define balanced forces *using your book or a dictionary.*

balanced forces ______________________________

New Vocabulary

Use your book or a dictionary to define the following terms.

axis of rotation ______________________________

period of rotation ______________________________

period of revolution ______________________________

ellipse ______________________________

astronomical unit ______________________________

planet ______________________________

Academic Vocabulary

Use your book or a dictionary to define force. *Then use the term in a scientific sentence.*

force ______________________________

____

Name ______________________________ Date ____________

Lesson 1 Structure of the Solar System (continued)

Main Idea | **Details**

What is the solar system?

I found this information on page ________.

Complete *the statement about the* solar system.

The solar system includes ______________________________

____

The Motion of Planets

I found this information on page ________.

Distinguish *between the* period of rotation *and the* period of revolution *of a planet. Define each term below.*

A planet's period of rotation is ______________________________

______________________________. A planet's period of revolution is ______________________________.

Kepler's Laws of Planetary Motion

I found this information on page ________.

Model *the* orbit of a planet. *Draw the planet's orbit according to* Kepler's first law.

Rephrase Kepler's second and third laws *in your own words.*

Kepler's Second Law: ______________________________

____

Kepler's Third Law: ______________________________

____

SUMMARIZE IT

Summarize one main idea from each section above.

____

____

____

Name _______________ Date _______________

Main Idea	Details
The Astronomical Unit *I found this information on page* ______.	**Analyze** *why the* astronomical unit *is used to measure distance in the solar system.* The astronomical unit is used because ______________________________ .
Gravity and the Solar System *I found this information on page* ______.	**Design** *a graphic organizer to summarize at least three key facts about gravity and its role in the solar system.* 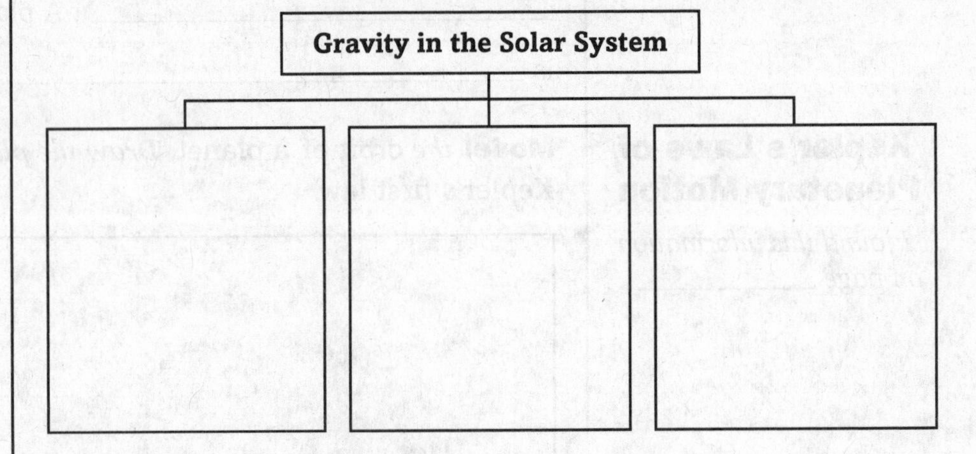
Formation of the Solar System *I found this information on page* ______.	**Sequence** *the events that* formed the solar system. **1.** A cloud of gas and dust called a nebula formed. **2.** ______ **3.** ______ **4.** ______ **5.** ______

SUMMARIZE IT

Summarize three main ideas from the above sections.

____

____

____

Name ______________________ Date __________

Our Solar System

Lesson 2 The Sun-Earth-Moon System

Grade 8 Science Content Standards—4.d: Students know that stars are the source of light for all bright objects in outer space and that the Moon and planets shine by reflected sunlight, not by their own light.

Scan *the headings, illustrations, and bold words in Lesson 2. Write three questions you have. Look for the answers as you read.*

1. ______________________
2. ______________________
3. ______________________

Review Vocabulary

Define gravity *using your book or a dictionary.*

gravity ______________________

New Vocabulary

Define *each term below using your book or a dictionary. Then use the terms in a short paragraph about the Moon.*

satellite ______________________

lunar phase ______________________

eclipse ______________________

Academic Vocabulary

Use a dictionary to define phase.

phase ______________________

Name ______________________ Date __________

Main Idea | **Details**

Earth's Motion Around the Sun

I found this information on page ________.

Organize *information about* Earth's orbit around the Sun. *Complete the concept map.*

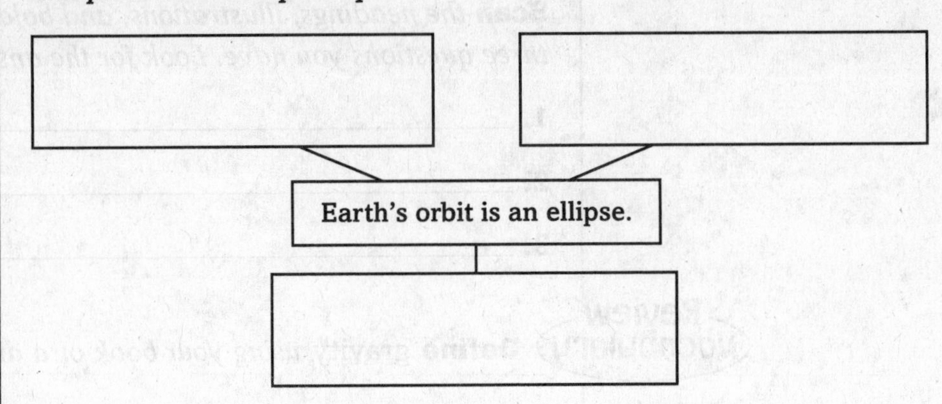

I found this information on page ________.

Complete *the statements below to describe* Earth's rotation.

Earth completes a rotation in about ________. Its axis is tilted at an angle of ________ to ________.

The Moon—Earth's Satellite

I found this information on page ________.

Sequence *the events that led to the* formation of the Moon, *according to the present theory.*

A large object ________________.

↓

____

↓

____

SUMMARIZE IT

Summarize three main ideas from the above sections.

____

____

____

Name ______________________ Date __________

Main Idea | **Details**

The Moon—Earth's Satellite

I found this information on page ________.

Create *a diagram showing the* phases of the Moon. *Include* Earth *and the* direction of sunlight. *Label each phase.*

Eclipses

I found this information on page ________.

Compare and contrast *a* solar eclipse *and a* lunar eclipse. *Complete the Venn diagram with at least six facts.*

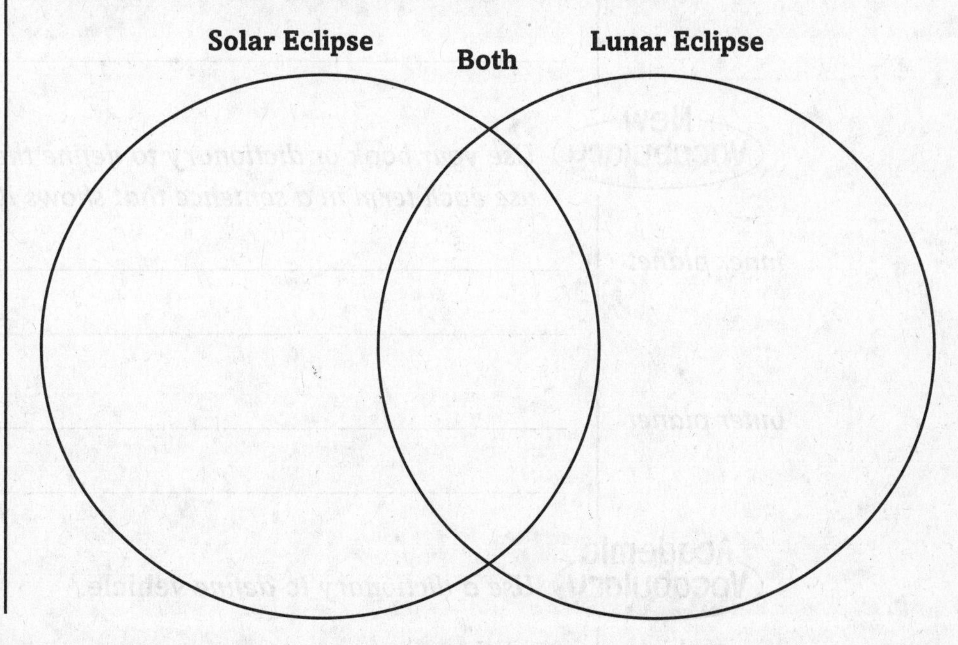

SUMMARIZE IT Choose one main idea from each of the above sections. Rephrase these ideas in your own words.

____

____

Name ______________________ Date __________

Our Solar System

Lesson 3 The Planets and Their Moons

Grade 8 Science Content Standards—4.e: Students know the appearance, general composition, relative position and size, and motion of objects in the solar system, including planets, planetary satellites, comets, and asteroids. Also covers: 4.d

Skim *Lesson 3. Write three ideas you discover as you skim the lesson.*

1. ______________________

2. ______________________

3. ______________________

Review Vocabulary

Define atmospheric pressure *using its scientific meaning.*

atmospheric pressure ______________________

New Vocabulary

Use your book or dictionary to define the following terms. Then use each term in a sentence that shows its scientific meaning.

inner planet ______________________

outer planet ______________________

Academic Vocabulary

Use a dictionary to define vehicle.

vehicle ______________________

Name ______________________________ Date ____________

Main Idea — Details

The Inner Planets

I found this information on page ________.

Summarize *key facts about* Mercury.

Diameter: ______________________________

Distance from Sun: ______________________________

Temperature: ______________________________

I found this information on page ________.

Compare and contrast Venus *and* Earth. *Complete the table.*

	Venus	Earth
Atmosphere		
Period of Rotation		
Period of Revolution		

I found this information on page ________.

Organize *information about* Mars. *Complete the concept map.*

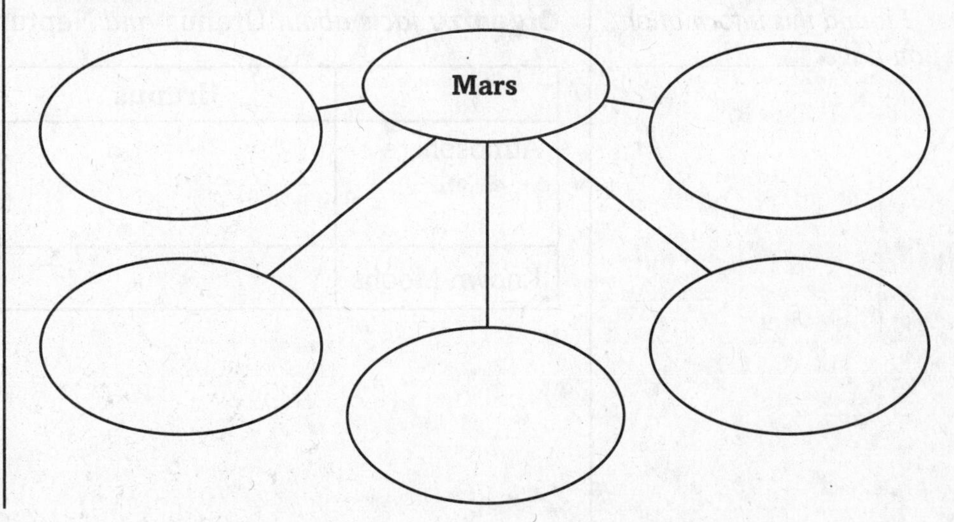

SUMMARIZE IT

Summarize one main idea about each inner planet.

____

____

____

Name ______________________ Date ____________

Main Idea	Details
The Outer Planets *I found this information on page ______.*	**Distinguish** *the 4* Galilean satellites of Jupiter. *Write one fact about each satellite.*
I found this information on page ______.	**Create** *a graphic organizer of key information about* Saturn.
I found this information on page ______.	**Organize** *facts about* Uranus *and* Neptune. *Complete the table.*

	Uranus	Neptune
Atmosphere		
Known Moons		

SUMMARIZE IT Summarize two main ideas from the above section.

Name ______________________ Date __________

Our Solar System

Lesson 4 Asteroids, Comets, and Meteroids

Grade 8 Science Content Standards—4.e: Students know the appearance, general composition, relative position and size, and motion of objects in the solar system, including planets, planetary satellites, comets, and asteroids.

Predict *three topics that will be covered in Lesson 4. Use the section headings to help.*

1. ______________________

2. ______________________

3. ______________________

Review Vocabulary

Define erosion *using your book or a dictionary.*

erosion ______________________

New Vocabulary

Use your book or a dictionary to define each term.

asteroid ______________________

comet ______________________

meteoroid ______________________

Academic Vocabulary

Use a dictionary to define impact. *Then use it in a sentence to reflect its scientific meaning.*

impact ______________________

Name ____________________ Date __________

Main Idea | **Details**

Asteroids

I found this information on page ________.

Organize *information about* asteroids. *Complete the concept map.*

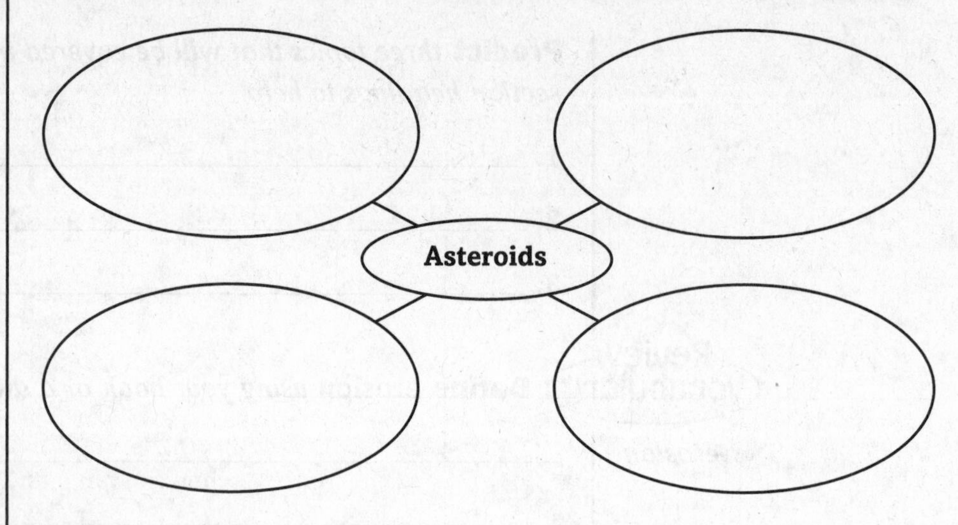

Comets

I found this information on page ________.

Model the parts of a comet. *Draw a comet as it travels away from the Sun. Use the words below to label your drawing.*

coma nucleus dust tail ion tail

Summarize *the* discoveries made by *Deep Impact.*

____

____

____

SUMMARIZE IT Rephrase the main ideas of the above sections.

____

____

____

____

Name ______________________________ Date __________

Main Idea | **Details**

Comets

I found this information on page ______.

Complete *the concept map about* Kuiper Belt objects.

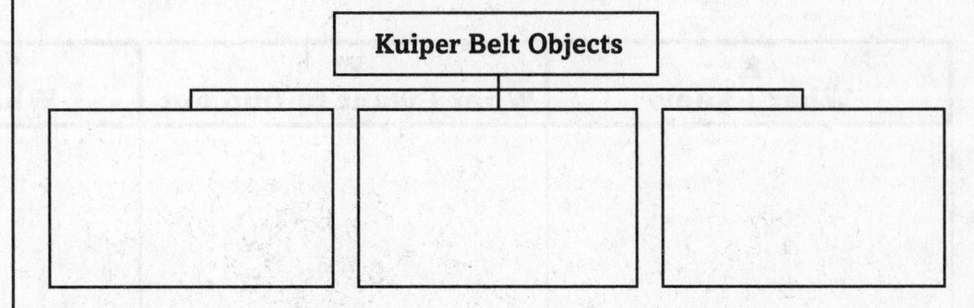

Meteoroids

I found this information on page ______.

Sequence *the formation of* meteoroids *and what happens when they reach Earth. Complete the flow chart.*

Meteoroids formed when a small planet broke apart during ______________________.

↓

Pieces of this planet ______________________.

↙ ↘

Most ______________________ ______________________.

A few ______________________, forming ______________________.

SUMMARIZE IT Use three bullet points to summarize the main ideas of the above sections.

____

____

____

Name ____________________ Date __________

Our Solar System Chapter Wrap-Up

Review the ideas you listed in the table at the beginning of the chapter. Cross out any incorrect information in the first column. Then complete the table by filling in the third column.

K What I know	W What I want to find out	L What I learned

Review

Use this checklist to help you study.

- ☐ Review the information you included in your Foldable.
- ☐ Study your *Science Notebook* on this chapter.
- ☐ Study the definitions of vocabulary words.
- ☐ Review daily homework assignments.
- ☐ Re-read the chapter and review the charts, graphs, and illustrations.
- ☐ Review the Standards Check at the end of each lesson.
- ☐ Look over the Standards Review at the end of the chapter.

SUMMARIZE IT **After reading this chapter, write four sentences summarizing its main ideas.**

____

____

____

____

Name ______________________________ Date ____________

Stars and Galaxies

Grade 8 Science Content Standards—4.b: Students know that the Sun is one of many stars in the Milky Way galaxy and that stars may differ in size, temperature, and color. Also covers: 2.g, 4.a, 4.c, 4.d

Before You Read

Before you read the chapter, think about what you already know about the topic. List three things that you already know about stars and galaxies in the first column. Then list three things that you would like to learn about stars and galaxies in the second column.

K What I know	W What I want to find out

FOLDABLES™ Study Organizer

Construct the Foldable as directed at the beginning of this chapter.

Science Journal

Write a short paragraph describing where you think stars are located relative to the solar system.

Name ______________________ Date ______________

Stars and Galaxies

Lesson 1 Stars

Grade 8 Science Content Standards—4.b: Students know that the Sun is one of many stars in the Milky Way galaxy and that stars may differ in size, temperature, and color. Also covers: 4.c, 4.d

Predict *three topics that will be discussed in Lesson 1 as you scan the headings and illustrations.*

1. ______________________

2. ______________________

3. ______________________

Review Vocabulary

Use your book to define spectral line.

spectral line ______________________

New Vocabulary

Use your book to define the following terms. Then write an original sentence that contains each term.

light-year ______________________

luminosity ______________________

apparent magnitude ______________________

absolute magnitude ______________________

Academic Vocabulary

Use a dictionary to define element. *Then use it in a sentence to show its scientific meaning.*

element ______________________

Name ________________________________ Date ____________

Main Idea | **Details**

What are stars?

I found this information on page ________.

Distinguish *between the layers of a star by describing each one.*

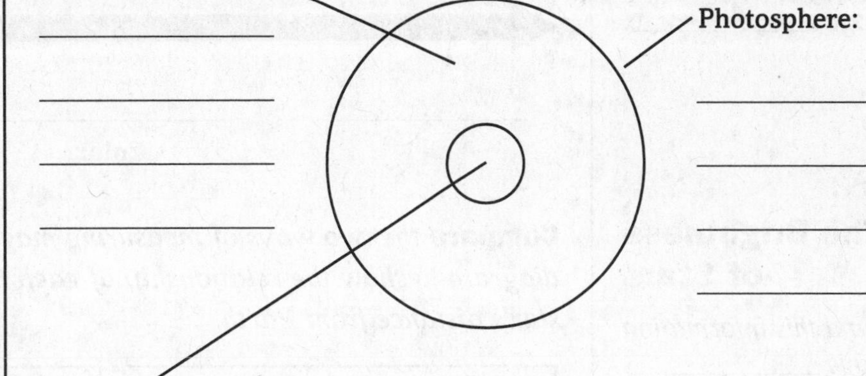

Core: ________________________________

I found this information on page ________.

Compare *the light-year with other units.*

One light-year is about equal to ________ kilometers / ________ AU

What are stars made of?

I found this information on page ________.

Define *the two types of spectra listed below.*

Continuous spectrum: ________________________________

Absorption spectrum: ________________________________

SUMMARIZE IT Summarize the three main ideas of the above sections with three bullet points.

____

____

____

Name ______________________ Date __________

Main Idea	Details
Temperature and Color of Stars *I found this information on page ______.*	**Sequence** *the colors of stars by temperature.* Temperature: Cooler ⟷ Hotter; ______ ______ ______ Color
The Brightness of Stars *I found this information on page ______.*	**Compare** *the two ways of measuring magnitude by completing the diagram to show the relationship of each type of magnitude to a star's distance from Earth.* Apparent magnitude ______ ______ ______ ______. / Absolute magnitude ______ ______ ______ ______.
Classifying Stars—The H-R Diagram *I found this information on page ______.*	**Classify** *the different types of stars on the Hertzsprung-Russell diagram by completing the table below.*

Type of Star	Description
Main sequence	
Red giant	
Supergiant	
White dwarf	

SUMMARIZE IT

Summarize two main ideas of the above sections.

____

____

Name ______________________ Date ____________

Stars and Galaxies

Lesson 2 How Stars Shine

Grade 8 Science Content Standards—2.g: Students know the role of gravity in forming and maintaining the shapes of planets, stars, and the solar system. Also covers: 4.d

Skim *through Lesson 2 of your book. Write three questions that come to mind from reading the headings and examining the illustrations.*

1. ______________________
2. ______________________
3. ______________________

Review Vocabulary *Use your book or a dictionary to define* pressure.

pressure ______________________

New Vocabulary *Use your book to define the following terms.*

nebula ______________________

nuclear fusion ______________________

red giant ______________________

white dwarf ______________________

supernova ______________________

neutron star ______________________

black hole ______________________

Academic Vocabulary *Use a dictionary to define* contract. *Then use it in a sentence to show its scientific meaning.*

contract ______________________

____

Name ______________________________ Date ____________

Main Idea | **Details**

How Stars Form

I found this information on page ________.

Sequence *the steps involved in the formation of a protostar.*

1. A nebula contains ____________ of high density.
2. ____________ causes particles to clump together.
3. The mass ____________ causing temperature to ____________.
4. The mass becomes ____________.
5. A ____________ is born.

How Stars Produce Light

I found this information on page ________.

Model *the steps involved in a* nuclear fusion *reaction that leads to a star's producing visible light. Sketch and label the steps.*

I found this information on page ________.

Analyze *how the forces of pressure and gravity act on a star.*

____

____

____

____

SUMMARIZE IT

Summarize the three main ideas of the above sections of this lesson with three bullet points.

____

____

____

Main Idea — Details

How Stars Come to an End

I found this information on page ________.

Compare *and* contrast *the formation of a* red giant *with that of a* white dwarf. *Include at least six facts in the Venn diagram.*

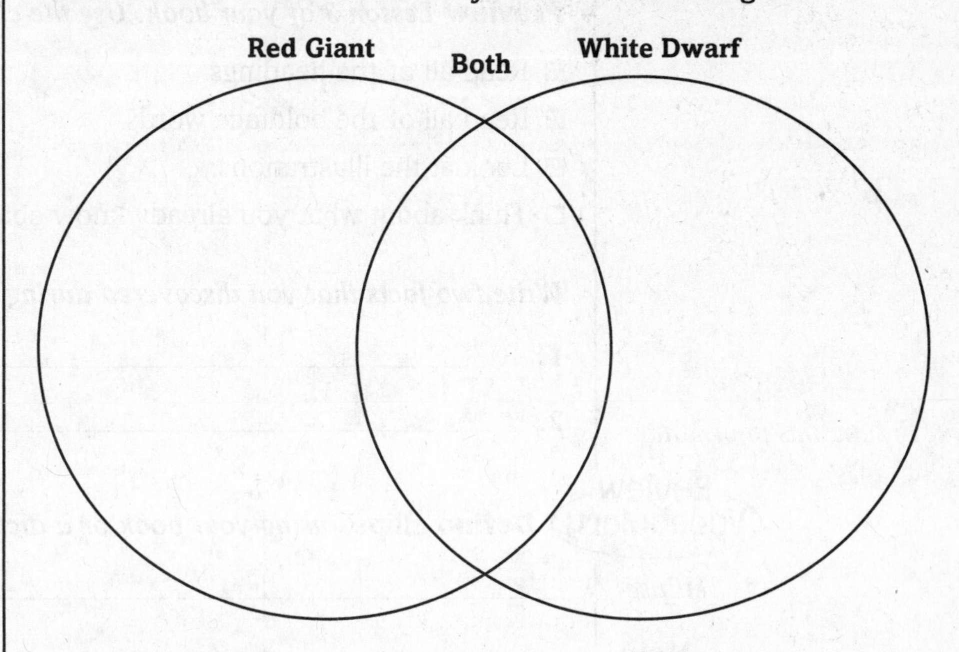

I found this information on page ________.

Organize *information about* neutron stars *and* black holes *by filling in the blanks.*

Neutron stars are made of ________________ ________________. The stars are very ________________ but very ________________. They form when ________________ and ________________ fuse to form ________________ in the core of a ________________. If a neutron star has a great enough mass, gravitational forces may be so strong that ________________ cannot escape. This is called a ________________.

SUMMARIZE IT

Highlight the main idea of this section in this passage.

When fusion stops within a star, there is no longer a balance between the forces of pressure and gravity. A star can collapse under the force of gravity. This can result in the formation of a white dwarf, a supernova, a neutron star, or a black hole.

Name ______________________ Date ______________

Stars and Galaxies

Lesson 3 Galaxies

Grade 8 Science Content Standards—4.a. Students know galaxies are clusters of billions of stars and may have different shapes. Also covers: 4.b, 4.c

Preview *Lesson 3 of your book. Use the checklist below.*

- ☐ Read all of the headings.
- ☐ Read all of the boldface words.
- ☐ Look at the illustrations.
- ☐ Think about what you already know about galaxies.

Write two facts that you discovered during your preview.

1. ______________________

2. ______________________

Review Vocabulary

Define ellipse *using your book or a dictionary.*

ellipse ______________________

New Vocabulary

Read the definition below. Write the correct vocabulary term on the blank to the left.

______________ theory that the universe began 14 billion years ago as a tiny point that expanded at great speed

Academic Vocabulary

Use a dictionary to define **randomly.**

randomly ______________________

____

Name ________________________ Date ____________

Main Idea **Details**

Stars Cluster in Galaxies and **Types of Galaxies**

I found this information on page ________.

Classify *the three major types of galaxies. Complete the table.*

Galaxy Type	Description
Spiral galaxy	
Elliptical galaxy	
Irregular galaxy	

I found this information on page ________.

Model *the Milky Way galaxy as it would appear if viewed from above. Indicate where the solar system lies within the galaxy.*

SUMMARIZE IT Summarize the main ideas of the above sections with two bullet points.

____

____

Name ______________________ Date __________

Main Idea — Details

The Distances Between Galaxies

I found this information on page ________.

Distinguish *between* galaxies, clusters, *and* superclusters *by completing the sentences.*

Galaxies

Galaxies are so far away that to the unaided eye the closest ones appear as ____________________. The closest galaxies to Earth are about ____________________.

are part of ↓

Clusters

Galaxies are not ____________ throughout the universe. Our galaxy is part of a cluster of galaxies called ________.

are part of ↓

Superclusters

A supercluster can spread across ____________ light-years.

The Big Bang Theory

I found this information on page ________.

Summarize *the* big bang theory.

____

____

____

____

____

____

SUMMARIZE IT

Summarize the two main ideas of the above sections with two bullet points.

____

____

Name ______________________________ Date __________

Tie It Together

Synthesize It

Construct a concept map that includes the following terms: clusters, stars, white dwarfs, galaxies, red giants, superclusters, main sequence stars, and universe. Construct the concept map so that it shows the relationship between the terms from the most inclusive to the least inclusive. Include key information for each of the terms in your map.

Name ______________________________ Date __________

Stars and Galaxies Chapter Wrap-Up

Review the ideas you listed in the table at the beginning of the chapter. Cross out any incorrect information in the first column. Then complete the table by filling in the third column.

K What I know	W What I want to find out	L What I learned

Review

Use this checklist to help you study.

- ☐ Review the information you included in your Foldable.
- ☐ Study your *Science Notebook* on this chapter.
- ☐ Study the definitions of vocabulary words.
- ☐ Review daily homework assignments.
- ☐ Re-read the chapter and review the charts, graphs, and illustrations.
- ☐ Review the Standards Check at the end of each lesson.
- ☐ Look over the Standards Review at the end of the chapter.

SUMMARIZE IT **After studying the chapter, list three important things you have learned about stars and galaxies.**

____

____

____

____